DEAD MAN'S PLACK
AN OLD THORN
AND
POEMS

DEAD MAN'S PLACK.

DEAD MAN'S PLACK AN OLD THORN & POEMS

BY

W. H. HUDSON

LONDON & TORONTO
J. M. DENT & SONS LTD.

Dead Man's Plack and *An Old Thorn* were first published in book form in 1920. The *Poems* were first collected in book form in the complete edition of W. H. Hudson's works, 1923–4, under the title of *A Little Boy Lost and Various Poems*; of these *The London Sparrow*, *In the Wilderness*, and *Gwendoline* appeared in *Merry England*, 1883–5.

Tecla and the Little Men is reprinted here by kind permission of Mr. Alfred Knopf.

CONTENTS

DEAD MAN'S PLACK

A

PREAMBLE

"THE insect tribes of human kind" is a mode of expression we are familiar with in the poets, moralists and other superior persons, or beings, who viewing mankind from their own vast elevation see us all more or less of one size and very, very small. No doubt the comparison dates back to early, probably Pliocene, times, when someone climbed to the summit of a very tall cliff, and looking down and seeing his fellows so diminished in size as to resemble insects, not so gross as beetles perhaps but rather like emmets, he laughed in the way they laughed then at the enormous difference between his stature and theirs. Hence the time-honoured and serviceable metaphor.

Now with me, in this particular instance, it was all the other way about—from insect to man—seeing that it was when occupied in watching the small comedies and tragedies of the insect world on its stage that I stumbled by chance upon a compelling reminder of one of the greatest tragedies in England's history—greatest, that is to say, in its consequences. And this is how it happened.

One summer day, prowling in an extensive oak wood, in Hampshire, known as Harewood Forest, I discovered that it counted among its inhabitants no fewer than three species of insects of peculiar interest to me, and from that time I haunted it, going there day after day to spend long hours in pursuit of my small quarry. Not to kill and preserve their diminutive corpses in a cabinet, but solely to witness the comedy of their brilliant little lives. And as I used to take my luncheon in my pocket I fell into the habit of going to a particular spot, some opening in the dense wood with a big tree to lean against and give me shade, where after refreshing myself with food and drink I could smoke my pipe in solitude and peace. Eventually I came to prefer one spot for my mid-day rest in the central part of the wood, where a stone cross, slender, beautifully proportioned and about eighteen feet high, had been erected some seventy or eighty years before by the lord of the manor. On one side of the great stone block on which the cross stood there was an inscription which told that it was placed there to mark the spot known from old as Dead Man's Plack; that, according to tradition, handed from father to son, it was just here that King Edgar slew his friend and favourite Earl Athelwold, when hunting in the forest.

I had sat there on many occasions, and had glanced from time to time at the inscription cut on the stone, once actually reading it, without having my attention drawn away from the insect world I was living in. It was not the tradition of the Saxon king nor the beauty of the cross in that green wilderness which drew me daily to the spot, but its solitariness and the little open space where I could sit in the shade and have my rest.

Then something happened. Some friends from town came down to me at the hamlet I was staying at, and one of the party, the mother of most of them, was not only older than the rest of us in years, but also in knowledge and wisdom; and at the same time she was younger than the youngest of us, since she had the curious mind, the undying interest in everything on earth—the secret, in fact, of everlasting youth. Naturally, being of this temperament, she wanted to know what I was doing and all about what I had seen, even to the minutest detail—the smallest insect—and in telling her of my days I spoke casually of the cross placed at a spot called Dead Man's Plack. This at once reminded her of something she had heard about it before, but long ago, in the seventies of last century; then presently it all came back to her, and it proved to me an interesting story.

It chanced that in that far back time she was in correspondence on certain scientific and literary subjects with a gentleman who was a native of this part of Hampshire in which we were staying, and that they got into a discussion about Freeman, the historian, during which he told her of an incident of his undergraduate days when Freeman was professor at Oxford. He attended a lecture by that man on the Mythical and Romantic Elements in Early English History, in which he stated for the guidance of all who study the past, that they must always bear in mind the inevitable passion for romance in men, especially the uneducated, and that when the student comes upon a romantic incident in early history, even when it accords with the known character of the person it relates to, he must reject it as false. Then, to rub the lesson in, he gave an account of the most flagrant of the romantic lies contained in the history of the Saxon kings. This was the story of King Edgar, and how his favourite, Earl Athelwold, deceived him as to the reputed beauty of Elfrida, and how Edgar in revenge slew Athelwold with his own hand when hunting. Then—to show how false it all was!—Edgar, the chronicles state, was at Salisbury and rode in one day to Harewood Forest, and there slew Athelwold. Now, said Freeman, as Harewood Forest is in Yorkshire, Edgar could not have ridden there from Salisbury in one day nor in two, nor in three, which was enough to show that the whole story was a fabrication.

The undergraduate, listening to the lecturer, thought the Professor was wrong owing to his ignorance of the fact that the Harewood Forest in which the deed was done was in Hampshire, within a day's ride from Salisbury, and that local tradition points to the very spot in the forest where Athelwold was slain. Accordingly he wrote to the Professor and gave him these facts. His letter was not answered; and the poor youth felt hurt, as he thought he was doing Professor Freeman a service by telling him something he didn't know. *He* didn't know his Professor Freeman.

This story about Freeman tickled me, because I dislike him, but if anyone were to ask me why I dislike him I should probably have to answer like a woman: Because I do. Or if stretched on the rack until I could find or invent a better reason I should perhaps say it was because he was so infernally cocksure, so convinced that he and he alone had the power of distinguishing between the true and false; also that he was so arbitrary and arrogant and ready to trample on those who doubted his infallibility.

All this, I confess, would not be much to say against him, seeing that it is nothing but the ordinary professorial or academic mind, and I suppose that the only difference between Freeman and the ruck of the professors was that he was more impulsive or articulate and had a greater facility in expressing his scorn.

Here I may mention in passing that when this lecture appeared in print in his *Historical Essays* he had evidently been put out a little, and also put on his mettle by that letter from an undergraduate, and had gone more deeply into the documents relating to the incident, seeing that he now relied mainly on the discrepancies in half a dozen chronicles he was able to point out to prove its falsity. His former main argument now appeared as a "small matter of detail"—a "confusion of geography" in the different versions of the old historians. But one tells us, Freeman writes, that Athelwold was killed in the Forest of Wherwell on his way to York, and then he says: "Now as Wherwell is in Hampshire, it could not be on the road to York"; and further on he says: "Now Harewood Forest in Yorkshire is certainly not the same as Wherwell in Hampshire," and so on, and on, and on, but always careful not to say that Wherwell Forest and Harewood Forest are two names for one and the same place, although now the name of Wherwell is confined to the village on the Test, where it is supposed Athelwold had his castle and lived with his wife before he was killed, and where Elfrida in her declining years, when trying to make her peace with God, came and built a Priory and took the habit herself and there finished her darkened life.

This then was how he juggled with words and documents and chronicles (his thimble-rigging), making a truth a lie or a lie a truth according as it suited a froward and prejudicate mind, to quote the expression of an older and simpler-minded historian —Sir Walter Raleigh.

Finally, to wind up the whole controversy, he says you are to take it as a positive truth that Edgar married Elfrida, and a positive falsehood that Edgar killed Athelwold. Why—seeing there is as good authority and reason for believing the one statement as the other? A foolish question! Why?—Because I, Professor or Pope Freeman, say so!

The main thing here is the effect the Freeman anecdote had on me, which was that when I went back to continue my insect-watching and rested at noon at Dead Man's Plack, the old legend would keep intruding itself on my mind, until, wishing to

have done with it, I said and I swore that it was true
—that the tradition preserved in the neighbourhood,
that on this very spot Athelwold was slain by the
king, was better than any document or history. It
was an act which had been witnessed by many
persons, and the memory of it preserved and handed
down from father to son for thirty generations; for
it must be borne in mind that the inhabitants of this
district of Andover and the villages on the Test have
never in the last thousand years been exterminated
or expelled. And ten centuries is not so long for an
event of so startling a character to persist in the
memory of the people when we consider that such
traditions have come down to us even from prehistoric
times and have proved true. Our archæologists, for
example, after long study of the remains, cannot tell
us how long ago—centuries or thousands of years
—a warrior with golden armour was buried under the
great cairn at Mold in Flintshire.

And now the curious part of all this matter comes
in. Having taken my side in the controversy and
made my pronouncement, I found that I was not
yet free of it. It remained with me, but in a new way
—not as an old story in old books, but as an event,
or series of events, now being re-enacted before my
very eyes. I actually saw and heard it all, from the
very beginning to the dreadful end; and this is what
I am now going to relate. But whether or not I shall
in my relation be in close accord with what history
tells us I know not, nor does it matter in the least.
For just as the religious mystic is exempt from the

study of theology and the whole body of religious doctrine, and from all the observances necessary to those who in fear and trembling are seeking their salvation, even so those who have been brought to the Gate of Remembrance are independent of written documents, chronicles and histories, and of the weary task of separating the false from the true. They have better sources of information. For I am not so vain as to imagine for one moment that without such external aid I am able to make shadows breathe, revive the dead, and know what silent mouths once said.

I

WHEN, sitting at noon in the shade of an oak tree at Dead Man's Plack, I beheld Edgar, I almost ceased to wonder at the miracle that had happened in this war-mad, desolated England, where Saxon and Dane, like two infuriated bull-dogs, were everlastingly at grips, striving to tear each other's throats out, and deluging the country with blood; how, ceasing from their strife, they had all at once agreed to live in peace and unity side by side under the young king; and this seemingly unnatural state of things endured even to the end of his life, on which account he was called Edgar the Peaceful.

He was beautiful in person and had infinite charm, and these gifts, together with his kingly qualities, which have won the admiration of all men of all ages, endeared him to his people. He was but thirteen when he came to be king of united England, and small for his age, but even in these terrible times he was remarkable for his courage, both physical and moral. Withal he had a subtle mind; indeed, I think he surpassed all our kings of the past thousand years in combining so many excellent qualities. His was the wisdom of the serpent combined with the gentleness—I will not say of the dove, but rather of the cat, our little tiger on the hearthrug, the most

beautiful of four-footed things, so lithe, so soft, of so
affectionate a disposition, yet capable when suddenly
roused to anger of striking with lightning rapidity
and rending the offender's flesh with its cruel,
unsheathed claws.

Consider the line he took, even as a boy! He
recognised among all those who surrounded him, in
his priestly adviser, the one man of so great a mind
as to be capable of assisting him effectually in ruling
so divided, war-loving and revengeful a people, and
he allowed him practically unlimited power to do
as he liked. He went even further by pretending to
fall in with Dunstan's ambitions of purging the
Church of the order of priests or half-priests, or
canons, who were in possession of most of the religious
houses in England, and were priests that married
wives and owned lands and had great power. Against
this monstrous state of things Edgar rose up in
his simulated wrath and cried out to Archbishop
Dunstan in a speech he delivered to sweep them
away and purify the Church and country from
such a scandal!

But Edgar himself had a volcanic heart, and to
witness it in full eruption it was only necessary to
convey to him the tidings of some woman of a rare
loveliness; and have her he would, in spite of all
laws human and divine. Thus when inflamed with
passion for a beautiful nun he did not hesitate to
smash the gates of a convent to drag her forth and
forcibly make her his mistress. And this, too, was a
dreadful scandal, but no great pother could be made

about it, seeing that Edgar was so powerful a friend
of the Church and of pure religion.

Now all the foregoing is contained in the histories,
but in what follows I have for sole light and guide
the vision that came to me at Dead Man's Plack,
and have only to add to this introductory note that
Edgar at the early age of twenty-two was a widower,
having already had to wife Ethelfled the Fair, who
was famous for her beauty, and who died shortly
after giving birth to a child who lived to figure later
in history as one of England's many Edwards.

NOW although King Edgar had dearly loved his wife, who was also beloved by all his people on account of her sweet and gentle disposition as well as of her exceeding beauty, it was not in his nature to brood long over such a loss. He had too keen a zest for life and the many interests and pleasures it had for him ever to become a melancholy man. It was a delight to him to be king, and to perform all kingly duties and offices. Also he was happy in his friends, especially in his favourite, the Earl Athelwold, who was like him in character, a man after his own heart. They were indeed like brothers, and some of those who surrounded the king were not too well pleased to witness this close intimacy. Both were handsome men, witty, of a genial disposition, yet under a light careless manner brave and ardent, devoted to the pleasure of the chase and all other pleasures, especially to those bestowed by golden Aphrodite, their chosen saint, albeit her name did not figure in the Calendar.

Hence it was not strange, when certain reports of the wonderful beauty of a woman in the West Country were brought to Edgar's ears, that his heart began to burn within him, and that by-and-by he opened himself to his friend on the subject. He told Athelwold that he had discovered the one woman in

England fit to be Ethelfled's successor, and that he
had resolved to make her his queen although he had
never seen her, since she and her father had never
been to court. That, however, would not deter him;
there was no other woman in the land whose claims
were equal to hers, seeing that she was the only
daughter and part heiress of one of the greatest men
in the kingdom, Ongar, Ealdorman of Devon and
Somerset, a man of vast possessions and great power.
Yet all that was of less account to him than her fame,
her personal worth, since she was reputed to be the
most beautiful woman in the land. It was for her
beauty that he desired her, and being of an exceedingly impatient temper in any case in which beauty
in a woman was concerned, he desired his friend to
proceed at once to Earl Ongar in Devon with an
offer of marriage to his daughter, Elfrida, from
the king.

Athelwold laughed at Edgar in this his most solemn
and kingly mood, and with a friend's privilege told
him not to be so simple as to buy a pig in a poke. The
lady, he said, had not been to court, consequently
she had not been seen by those best able to judge
of her reputed beauty. Her fame rested wholly on
the report of the people of her own country, who were
great as everyone knew at blowing their own trum-
pets. Their red and green county was England's
paradise; their men the bravest and handsomest
and their women the most beautiful in the land.
For his part he believed there were as good men and
as fair women in Mercia and East Anglia as in the

West. It would certainly be an awkward business
if the king found himself bound in honour to wed with
a person he did not like. Awkward because of her
father's fierce pride and power. A better plan would
be to send someone he could trust not to make a
mistake to find out the truth of the report.

Edgar was pleased at his friend's wise caution,
and praised him for his candour, which was that of
a true friend, and as he was the only man he could
thoroughly trust in such a matter he would send
him. Accordingly, Athelwold, still much amused at
Edgar's sudden wish to make an offer of marriage to
a woman he had never seen, set out on his journey
in great state with many attendants as befitted his
person and his mission, which was ostensibly to bear
greetings and loving messages from the king to some
of his most important subjects in the West Country.

In this way he travelled through Wilts, Somerset
and Devon, and in due time arrived at Earl Ongar's
castle on the Exe.

III

ATHELWOLD, who thought highly of himself, had undertaken his mission with a light heart, but now when his progress in the West had brought him to the great ealdorman's castle it was borne in on him that he had put himself in a very responsible position. He was here to look at this woman with cold, critical eyes, which was easy enough; and having looked at and measured and weighed her, he would make a true report to Edgar; that too would be easy for him, since all his power and happiness in life depended on the king's continual favour. But Ongar stood between him and the woman he had come to see and take stock of with that clear unbiased judgment which he could safely rely on. And Ongar was a proud and stern old man, jealous of his great position, who had not hesitated to say on Edgar's accession to the kingship, knowing well that his words would be reported in due time, that he refused to be one of the crowd who came flocking from all over the land to pay homage to a boy. It thus came about that neither then nor at any subsequent period had there been any personal relations between the king and this English subject, who was prouder than all the Welsh kings who had rushed at Edgar's call to make their submission.

But now when Ongar had been informed that the

king's intimate friend and confidant was on his way to him with greetings and loving messages from Edgar, he was flattered, and resolved to receive him in a friendly and loyal spirit and do him all the honour in his power. For Edgar was no longer a boy: he was king over all this hitherto turbulent realm, East and West from sea to sea and from the Land's End to the Tweed, and the strange enduring peace of the times was a proof of his power.

It thus came to pass that Athelwold's mission was made smooth to him, and when they met and conversed, the fierce old Earl was so well pleased with his visitor, that all trace of the sullen hostility he had cherished towards the court passed away like the shadow of a cloud. And later, in the banqueting-room, Athelwold came face to face with the woman he had come to look at with cold, critical eyes, like one who examines a horse in the interests of a friend who desires to become its purchaser.

Down to that fatal moment the one desire of his heart was to serve his friend faithfully in this delicate business. Now, the first sight of her, the first touch of her hand, wrought a change in him, and all thought of Edgar and of the purpose of his visit vanished out of his mind. Even he, one of the great nobles of his time, the accomplished courtier and life of the court, stood silent like a person spell-bound before this woman who had been to no court, but had lived always with that sullen old man in comparative seclusion in a remote province. It was not only the beautiful dignity and graciousness with which she received him, with the exquisite beauty in the lines and colour of her face, and her hair which, if unloosed, would have covered her to the knees as with a splendid mantle. That hair of a colour comparable only to that of the sweet gale when that sweet plant is in its golden withy or catkin stage in the month of May, and is clothed with catkins as with a foliage of a deep shining red gold, that seems not a colour of earth but rather one distilled from the sun itself. Nor was it the colour of her eyes, the deep pure blue of the lungwort, that blue loveliness seen in no other flower on earth. Rather it was the light from her eyes which was like lightning that pierced and startled him; for that light, that expression, was a living spirit looking through his eyes into the depths of his soul, knowing all its strength and weakness, and in the same instant resolving to make it her own and have dominion over it.

It was only when he had escaped from the power and magic of her presence, when alone in his sleeping room, that reflection came to him and the recollection of Edgar and of his mission. And there was dismay in the thought. For the woman was his, part and parcel of his heart and soul and life; for that was what her lightning glance had said to him, and she could not be given to another. No, not to the king! Had any man, any friend, ever been placed in so terrible a position? Honour? Loyalty? To whichever side he inclined he could not escape the crime, the base betrayal and abandonment! But loyalty to the king would be the greater crime. Had not Edgar himself broken every law of God and man to gratify his passion for a woman? Not a woman like this! Never would Edgar look on her until he, Athelwold, had obeyed her and his own heart and made her his for ever! And what would come then! He would not consider it—he would perish rather than yield her to another!

That was how the question came before him, and how it was settled, during the long sleepless hours when his blood was in a fever and his brain on fire; but when day dawned and his blood grew cold and his brain was tired, the image of Edgar betrayed and in a deadly rage became insistent, and he rose desponding and in dread of the meeting to come. And no sooner did he meet her than she overcame him as on the previous day; and so it continued during the whole period of his visit, racked with passion, drawn now to this side, now to that, and when he was most resolved to have her then most furiously assaulted by loyalty, by friendship, by honour, and he was like a stag at bay fighting for his life against the hounds. And every time he met her —and the passionate words he dared not speak were like confined fire, burning him up inwardly—seeing him pale and troubled she would greet him with a smile and look which told him she knew that he was troubled in heart, that a great conflict was raging in him, also that it was on her account and was perhaps because he had already bound himself to some other woman, some great lady of the land; and now this new passion had come to him. And her

smile and look were like the world-irradiating sun
when it rises, and the black menacing cloud that
brooded over his soul would fade and vanish, and
he knew that she had again claimed him and that
he was hers.

So it continued till the very moment of parting,
and again as on their first meeting he stood silent
and troubled before her; then in faltering words
told her that the thought of her would travel and be
with him; that in a little while, perhaps in a month
or two, he would be rid of a great matter which had
been weighing heavily on his mind, and once free
he could return to Devon, if she would consent to
his paying her another visit.

She replied smilingly with gracious words, with
no change from that exquisite perfect dignity which
was always hers; nor tremor in her speech, but only
that understanding look from her eyes, which said:
Yes, you shall come back to me in good time, when
you have smoothed the way, to claim me for your own.

IV

ON Athelwold's return the king embraced him warmly, and was quick to observe a change in him—the thinner, paler face and appearance generally of one lately recovered from a grievous illness or who had been troubled in mind. Athelwold explained that it had been a painful visit to him, due in the first place to the anxiety he experienced of being placed in so responsible a position, and in the second place the misery it was to him to be the guest for many days of such a person as the ealdorman, a man of a rough, harsh aspect and manner, who daily made himself drunk at table, after which he would grow intolerably garrulous and boastful. Then, when his host had been carried to bed by his servants, his own wakeful, troubled hours would begin. For at first he had been struck by the woman's fine, handsome presence, albeit she was not the peerless beauty she had been reported; but when he had seen her often and more closely and had conversed with her he had been disappointed. There was something lacking; she had not the softness, the charm, desirable in a woman; she had something of her parent's harshness, and his final judgment was that she was not a suitable person for the king to marry.

Edgar was a little downcast at first, but quickly

recovering his genial manner, thanked his friend for having served him so well.

For several weeks following the king and the king's favourite were constantly together; and during that period Athelwold developed a peculiar sweetness and affection towards Edgar, often recalling to him their happy boyhood's days in East Anglia, when they were like brothers, and cemented the close friendship which was to last them for the whole of their lives. Finally, when it seemed to his watchful, crafty mind that Edgar had cast the whole subject of his wish to marry Elfrida into oblivion, and that the time was now ripe for carrying out his own scheme, he re-opened the subject, and said that although the lady was not a suitable person to be the king's wife it would be good policy on his, Athelwold's, part, to win her on account of her position as only daughter and part heiress of Ongar, who had great power and possessions in the West. But he would not move in the matter without Edgar's consent.

Edgar, ever ready to do anything to please his friend, freely gave it, and only asked him to give an assurance that the secret object of his former visit to Devon would remain inviolate. Accordingly Athelwold took a solemn oath that it would never be revealed, and Edgar then slapped him on the back and wished him God-speed in his wooing.

Very soon after thus smoothing the way, Athelwold returned to Devon, and was once more in the presence of the woman who had so enchanted him, with that same meaning smile on her lips and light in her eyes

which had been her good-bye and her greeting, only
now it said to him: You have returned as I knew you
would, and I am ready to give myself to you.

From every point of view it was a suitable union,
seeing that Athelwold would inherit power and great
possessions from his father, Ealdorman of East
Anglia, and before long the marriage took place,
and by-and-by Athelwold took his wife to Wessex,
to the castle he had built for himself on his estate
of Wherwell, on the Test. There they lived together,
and as they had married for love they were happy.
But as the king's intimate friend and the
companion of many of his frequent journeys he could
not always bide with her nor be with her for any great
length of time. For Edgar had a restless spirit and
was exceedingly vigilant, and liked to keep a watchful eye on the different lately hostile nations of
Mercia, East Anglia, and Northumbria, so that his
journeys were frequent and long to these distant parts
of his kingdom. And he also had his naval forces to
inspect at frequent intervals. Thus it came about
that he was often absent from her for weeks and
months at a stretch. And so the time went on, and
during these long absences a change would come
over Elfrida; the lovely colour, the enchanting
smile, the light of her eyes—the outward sign of an
intense brilliant life—would fade, and with eyes cast
down she would pace the floors or the paths or sit
brooding in silence by the hour.

Of all this Athelwold knew nothing, since she made
no complaint, and when he returned to her the light

and life and brilliance would be hers again, and
there was no cloud or shadow on his delight. But
the cloud would come back over her when he again
went away. Her only relief in her condition was to
sit before a fire or when out of doors to seat herself
on the bank of the stream and watch the current.
For although it was still summer, the month being
August, she would have a fire of logs lighted in a
large chamber and sit staring at the flames by the
hour, and sometimes holding her outstretched hands
before the flames until they were hot, she would
then press them to her lips. Or when the day was
warm and bright she would be out of doors and spend
hours by the river gazing at the swift crystal current
below as if fascinated by the sight of the running
water. It is a marvellously clear water, so that
looking down on it you can see the rounded pebbles
in all their various colours and markings lying at
the bottom, and if there should be a trout lying there
facing the current and slowly waving his tail from
side to side, you could count the red spots on his
side, so clear is the water. Even more did the floating
water-grass hold her gaze—that bright green grass
that, rooted in the bed of the stream, sends its thin
blades to the surface where they float and wave like
green floating hair. Stooping, she would dip a hand
in the stream and watch the bright clear water
running through the fingers of her white hand, then
press the hand to her lips.

Then again when day declined she would quit the
stream to sit before the blazing logs, staring at the

flames. What am I doing here? she would murmur. And what is this my life? When I was at home in Devon I had a dream of Winchester, of Salisbury, or other great towns further away, where the men and women who are great in the land meet together, and where my eyes would perchance sometimes have the happiness to behold the king himself—my husband's close friend and companion. My waking has brought a different scene before me; this castle in the wilderness, a solitude where from an upper window I look upon leagues of forest, a haunt of wild animals. I see great birds soaring in the sky and listen to the shrill screams of kite and buzzard; and sometimes when lying awake on a still night the distant long howl of a wolf. Also, it is said, there are great stags, and roe-deer, and wild boars, and it is Athelwold's joy to hunt them and slay them with his spear. A joy too when he returns from the hunt or from a long absence to play with his beautiful wife—his caged bird of pretty feathers and a sweet song to soothe him when he is tired. But of his life at court he tells me little, and of even that little I doubt the truth. Then he leaves me and I am alone with his retainers—the crowd of serving men and women and the armed men to safeguard me. I am alone with my two friends which I have found, one out of doors, the other in—the river which runs at the bottom of the ground where I take my walks, and the fire I sit before. The two friends, companions, and lovers to whom all the secrets of my soul are confided. I love them, having no other in

the world to love, and here I hold my hand before
the flames until it is hot and then kiss the heat, and
by the stream I kiss my wetted hands. And if I were
to remain here until this life became unendurable I
should consider as to which one of these two lovers
I should give myself. This one I think is too ardent
in his love—it would be terrible to be wrapped round
in his fiery arms and feel his fiery mouth on mine.
I should rather go to the other one to lie down on
his pebbly bed, and give myself to him to hold me
in his cool, shining arms and mix his green hair with
my loosened hair. But my wish is to live and not
die. Let me then wait a little longer; let me watch
and listen, and perhaps some day, by-and-by, from
his own lips, I shall capture the secret of this my
caged solitary life.

And the very next day Athelwold, having just
returned with the king to Salisbury, was once more
with her; and the brooding cloud had vanished from
her life and countenance; she was once more his
passionate bride, lavishing caresses on him, listening
with childish delight to every word that fell from
his lips, and desiring no other life and no greater
happiness than this.

V

IT was early September, and the king with some
of the nobles who were with him, after hunting
the deer over against Cranbourne, returned at
evening to Salisbury, and after meat with some of
his intimates they sat late drinking wine and fell
into a merry, boisterous mood. They spoke of Athelwold, who was not with them, and indulged in some
mocking remarks about his frequent and prolonged
absences from the king's company. Edgar took it
in good part and smilingly replied that it had been
reported to him that the earl was now wedded to a
woman with a will. Also he knew that her father,
the great Ealdorman of Devon, had been famed for
his tremendous physical strength. It was related
of him that he had once been charged by a furious
bull, that he had calmly waited the onset and had
dealt the animal a staggering blow with his fist on
its head and had then taken it up in his arms and
hurled it into the river Exe. If, he concluded, the
daughter had inherited something of this power it
was not to be wondered at that she was able to detain
her husband at home.

Loud laughter followed this pleasantry of the
king's, then one of the company remarked that not
a woman's will, though it might be like steel of the
finest temper, nor her muscular power, would serve

to change Athelwold's nature or keep him from his friend, but only a woman's exceeding beauty.

Then Edgar, seeing that he had been put upon the defence of his absent friend, and that all of them were eager to hear his next word, replied that there was no possession a man was prouder of than that of a beautiful wife; that it was more to him than his own best qualities, his greatest actions, or than titles and lands and gold. If Athelwold had indeed been so happy as to secure the most beautiful woman he would have been glad to bring her to court to exhibit her to all—friends and foes alike—for his own satisfaction and glory.

Again they greeted his speech with laughter, and one cried out: "Do you believe it?"

Then another, bolder still, exclaimed: "It's God's truth that she is the fairest woman in the land—perhaps no fairer has been in any land since Helen of Troy. This I can swear to," he added, smiting the board with his hand, "because I have it from one who saw her at her home in Devon before her marriage. One who is a better judge in such matters than I am or than anyone at this table, not excepting the king, seeing that he is not only gifted with the serpent's wisdom but with that creature's cold blood as well."

Edgar heard him frowningly, then ended the discussion by rising, and silence fell on the company, for all saw that he was offended. But he was not offended with them, since they knew nothing of his and Athelwold's secret, and what they thought and felt about his friend was nothing to him. But these fatal words about Elfrida's beauty had pierced him with a sudden suspicion of his friend's treachery. And Athelwold was the man he greatly loved—the companion of all his years since their boyhood together. Had he betrayed him in this monstrous way—wounding him in his tenderest part? The very thought that such a thing might be was like a madness in him. Then he reflected—then he remembered, and said to himself: Yes, let me follow his teaching in this matter too, as in the other, and exercise caution and look before I leap. I shall look and look well and see and judge for myself.

The result was that when his boon companions next met him there was no shadow of displeasure in him; he was in a peculiarly genial mood, and so continued. And when his friend returned he embraced him and gently upbraided him for having kept away for so long a time. He begged him to remember that he was his one friend and confidant who was more than a brother to him, and that if wholly deprived of his company he would regard himself as the loneliest man in the kingdom. Then in a short time he spoke once more in the same strain, and said he had not yet sufficiently honoured his friend before the world, and that he proposed visiting him at his own castle to make the acquaintance of his wife and spend a day with him hunting the boar in Harewood Forest.

Athelwold, secretly alarmed, made a suitable reply, expressing his delight at the prospect of receiving the king, and begging him to give him a couple of days' notice before making his visit, so as to give him time to make all preparation for his entertainment.

This the king promised, and also said that this would be an informal visit to a friend, that he would go alone with some of his servants and huntsmen and ride there one day, hunt the next day and return to Salisbury on the third day. And a little later, when the day of his visit was fixed on, Athelwold returned in haste with an anxious mind to his castle.

Now his hard task and the most painful moment of his life had come. Alone with Elfrida in her chamber he cast himself down before her, and with his bowed head resting on her knees, made a clean breast of the whole damning story of the deceit he had practised towards the king in order to win her for himself. In anguish and shedding tears he implored her forgiveness, begging her to think of that irresistible power of love she had inspired in him, which would have made it worse than death to see her the wife of another—even of Edgar himself—his friend, the brother of his soul. Then he went on to speak of Edgar, who was of a sweet and lovable nature, yet capable of a deadly fury against those who offended him; and this was an offence he would take more to heart than any other; he would be implacable if he once thought that he had been wilfully deceived, and she only could now save them from certain destruction. For now it seemed to him that Edgar had conceived a suspicion that the account he had of her was not wholly true, which was that she was a handsome woman but not surpassingly beautiful as had been reputed, not graceful, not charming in manner and conversation.   She could save them by justifying his description of her—by using a woman's art to lessen instead of enhancing her natural beauty, by putting away her natural charm and power to fascinate all who approached her.

Thus he pleaded, praying for mercy, even as a captive prays to his conqueror for life, and never once daring to lift his bowed head to look at her face; while she sat motionless and silent, not a word, not a sigh, escaping her; and she was like a woman carved in stone, with knees of stone on which his head rested.

Then, at length, exhausted with his passionate pleading and frightened at her silence and deadly stillness, he raised his head and looked up at her face to behold it radiant and smiling.   Then, looking down lovingly into his eyes, she raised her hands to her head, and loosening the great mass of coiled tresses let them fall over him, covering his head and shoulders and back as with a splendid mantle of shining red gold.   And he, the awful fear now gone, continued silently gazing up at her, absorbed in her wonderful loveliness.

Bending down she put her arms round his neck and spoke: "Do you not know, O Athelwold, that I love you alone and could love no other, noble or king; that without you life would not be life to me? All you have told me endears you more to me, and all you wish me to do shall be done, though it may cause your king and friend to think meanly of you for having given your hand to one so little worthy of you."

She having thus spoken, he was ready to pour forth his gratitude in burning words, but she would not have it. "No more words," she said, putting her hand on his mouth. "Your anxious day is over—your burden dropped. Rest here on the couch by my side, and let me think on all there is to plan and do against to-morrow evening."

And so they were silent, and he, reclining on the cushions, watched her face and saw her smile and wondered what was passing in her mind to cause that smile. Doubtless it was something to do with the question of her disguising arts.

What had caused her to smile was a happy memory of the days with Athelwold before their marriage, when one day he came in to her with a leather bag in his hand and said: "Do you, who are so beautiful yourself, love all beautiful things? And do you love the beauty of gems?" And when she replied that she loved gems above all beautiful things, he poured out the contents of his bag in her lap—brilliants, sapphires, rubies, emeralds, opals, pearls in gold setting, in bracelets, necklets, pendants, rings and brooches. And when she gloated over this splendid gift, taking up gem after gem, exclaiming delightedly at its size and colour and lustre, he told her that he once knew a man who maintained that it was a mistake for a beautiful woman to wear gems. Why? she asked;

c

would he have them wholly unadorned? No, he replied, he liked to see them wearing gold, saying that gold makes the most perfect setting for a woman's beauty, just as it does for a precious stone, and its effect is to enhance the beauty it surrounds. But the woman's beauty has its meeting and central point in the eyes, and the light and soul in them illumines the whole face. And in the stone nature simulates the eye, and although without a soul its brilliant light and colour make it the equal of the eye, and therefore when worn as an ornament it competes with the eye, and in effect lessens the beauty it is supposed to enhance. He said that gems should be worn only by women who are not beautiful, who must rely on something extraneous to attract attention, since it would be better to a homely woman that men should look at her to admire a diamond or sapphire than not to look at her at all. She had laughed and asked him who the man was who had such strange ideas, and he had replied that he had forgotten his name.

Now, recalling this incident after so long a time, it all at once flashed into her mind that Edgar was the man he had spoken of; she knew now because, always secretly watchful, she had noted that he never spoke of Edgar or heard Edgar spoken of without a slight subtle change in the expression of his face, also, if he spoke, in the tone of his voice. It was the change that comes into the face, and into the tone, when one remembers or speaks of the person most loved in all the world. And she remembered now that he had that changed expression and tone of voice, when he had spoken of the man whose name he pretended to have forgotten.

And while she sat thinking of this it grew dark in the room, the light of the fire having died down. Then presently, in the profound stillness of the room, she heard the sound of his deep, regular breathing and knew that he slept, and that it was a sweet sleep after his anxious day. Going softly to the hearth she moved the yet still glowing logs, until they sent up a sudden flame and the light fell upon the sleeper's still face. Turning, she gazed steadily at it—the face of the man who had won her; but her own face in the firelight was white and still and wore a strange expression. Now she moved noiselessly to his side and bent down as if to whisper in his ear, but suddenly drew back again and moved towards the door, then turning gazed once more at his face and murmured: "No, no, even a word faintly whispered would bring him a dream, and it is better his sleep should be dreamless. For now he has had his day and it is finished, and to-morrow is mine."

VI

ON the following day Athelwold was occupied with preparations for the king's reception and for the next day's boar-hunt in the forest. At the same time he was still somewhat anxious as to his wife's more difficult part, and from time to time he came to see and consult with her. He then observed a singular change in her, both in her appearance and conduct. No longer the radiant, loving Elfrida, her beauty now had been dimmed and she was unsmiling and her manner towards him repellent. She had nothing to say to him except that she wished him to leave her alone. Accordingly he withdrew, feeling a little hurt, and at the same time admiring her extraordinary skill in disguising her natural loveliness and charm, but almost fearing that she was making too great a change in her appearance.

Thus passed the day, and in the late afternoon Edgar duly arrived, and when he had rested a little, was conducted to the banqueting-room, where the meeting with Elfrida would take place.

Then Elfrida came, and Athelwold hastened to the entrance to take her hand and conduct her to the king; then, seeing her, he stood still and stared in silent astonishment and dismay at the change he saw in her, for never before had he beheld her so beautiful, so queenly and magnificent. What did it mean—did she wish to destroy him? Seeing the state he was in she placed her hand in his, and murmured softly: I know best. And so, holding her hand, he conducted her to the king, who stood waiting to receive her. For all she had done that day to please and to deceive him had now been undone, and everything that had been possible had been done to enhance her loveliness. She had arrayed herself in a violet-coloured silk gown with a network of gold thread over the body and wide sleeves to the elbows, and a rope of gold round her waist with its long ends falling to her knee. The great mass of her coiled hair was surmounted with a golden comb, and golden pendants dropped from her ears to her shoulders. Also she wore gold armlets coiled serpent-wise round her white arms from elbow to wrist. Not a gem—nothing but pale yellow gold.

Edgar himself was amazed at her loveliness, for never had he seen anything comparable to it; and when he gazed into her eyes she did not lower hers, but returned gaze for gaze, and there was that in her eyes and their strange eloquence which kindled a sudden flame of passion in his heart, and for a moment it appeared in his countenance. Then, quickly recovering himself, he greeted her graciously but with his usual kingly dignity of manner, and for the rest of the time he conversed with her and Athelwold in such a pleasant and friendly way that his host began to recover somewhat from his apprehensions. But in his heart Edgar was saying: And

this is the woman that Athelwold, the close friend
of all my days, from boyhood until now, the one
man in the world I loved and trusted, has robbed
me of!

And Athelwold at the same time was revolving
in his mind the mystery of Elfrida's action. What
did she mean when she whispered to him that she
knew best? And why, when she wished to appear
in that magnificent way before the king, had she
worn nothing but gold ornaments—not one of the
splendid gems of which she possessed such a store?

She had remembered something which he had
forgotten.

Now when the two friends were left alone together
drinking wine, Athelwold was still troubled in his
mind, although his suspicion and fear were not so
acute as at first, and the longer they sat talking—
until the small hours—the more relieved did he feel
from Edgar's manner towards him. Edgar in his
cups opened his heart and was more loving and free
in his speech than ever before. He loved Athelwold
as he loved no one else in the world, and to see him
great and happy was his first desire; and he con-
gratulated him from his heart on having found a
wife who was worthy of him and would eventually
bring him, through her father, such great possessions
as would make him the chief nobleman in the land.
All happiness and glory to them both; and when
a child was born to them he would be its godfather,
and if happily by that time there was a queen, she
should be its godmother.

Then he recalled their happy boyhood's days in East Anglia, that joyful time when they first hunted and had many a mishap and fell from their horses when they pursued hare and deer and bustard in the wide open stretches of sandy country; and in the autumn and winter months when they were wild-fowling in the great level flooded lands where the geese and all wild-fowl came in clouds and myriads. And now he laughed and now his eyes grew moist at the recollection of the irrecoverable glad days.

Little time was left for sleep; yet they were ready early next morning for the day's great boar-hunt in the forest, and only when the king was about to mount his horse did Elfrida make her appearance. She came out to him from the door, not richly dressed now, but in a simple white linen robe and not an ornament on her except that splendid crown of the red-gold hair on her head. And her face too was almost colourless now, and grave and still. She brought wine in a golden cup and gave it to the king, and he once more fixed his eyes on her and for some moments they continued silently gazing, each in that fixed gaze seeming to devour the secrets of the other's soul. Then she wished him a happy hunting, and he said in reply he hoped it would be the happiest hunting he had ever had. Then, after drinking the wine, he mounted his horse and rode away. And she remained standing very still, the cup in her hand, gazing after him as he rode side by side with Athelwold, until in the distance the trees hid him from her sight.

Now when they had ridden a distance of three miles or more into the heart of the forest, they came to a broad drive-like stretch of green turf, and the king cried: "This is just what I have been wishing for! Come, let us give our horses a good gallop." And when they loosened the reins, the horses, glad to have a race on such a ground, instantly sprang forward; but Edgar, keeping a tight rein, was presently left twenty or thirty yards behind; then, setting spurs to his horse, he dashed forward, and on coming abreast of his companion, drew his knife and struck him in the back, dealing the blow with such a concentrated fury that the knife was buried almost to the hilt. Then violently wrenching it out, he would have struck again had not the earl, with a scream of agony, tumbled from his seat. The horse, freed from its rider, rushed on in a sudden panic, and the king's horse side by side with it. Edgar, throwing himself back and exerting his whole strength, succeeded in bringing him to a stop at a distance of fifty or sixty yards, then turning, came riding back at a furious speed.

Now when Athelwold fell, all those who were riding behind, the earl's and the king's men to the number of thirty or forty, dashed forward, and some of them, hurriedly dismounting, gathered about him as he lay groaning and writhing and pouring out his blood on the ground. But at the king's approach they drew quickly back to make way for him, and he came straight on and caused his horse to trample on the fallen man. Then pointing to him with the knife he still had in his hand, he cried: "That is how I serve a false friend and traitor!" Then, wiping the stained knife-blade on his horse's neck and sheathing it, he shouted: "Back to Salisbury!" and setting spurs to his horse, galloped off towards the Andover road.

His men immediately mounted and followed, leaving the earl's men with their master. Lifting him up, they placed him on a horse, and with a mounted man on each side to hold him up, they moved back at a walking pace towards Wherwell.

Messengers were sent ahead to inform Elfrida of what had happened, and then, an hour later, yet another messenger to tell that Athelwold, when half-way home, had breathed his last. Then at last the corpse was brought to the castle and she met it with tears and lamentations. But afterwards in her own chamber, when she had dismissed all her attendants, as she desired to weep alone, her grief changed to joy. O, glorious Edgar, she said, the time will come when you will know what I feel now, when at your feet, embracing your knees and kissing the blessed hand that with one blow has given me life and liberty. One blow and your revenge was satisfied and you had won me; I know it, I saw it all in that flame of love and fury in your eyes at our first meeting, which you permitted me to see, which, if he had seen, he would have known that he was doomed. O perfect master of dissimulation, all the more do I love and worship you for dealing with him as he dealt with you and with me; caressing him with flattering words until the moment came to strike and slay. And I love you all the more for making your horse trample on him as he lay bleeding his life out on the ground. And now you have opened the way with your knife you shall come back or call me to you when it pleases you, and for the rest of your life it will be a satisfaction to you to know that you have taken a modest woman as well as the fairest in the land for wife and queen, and your pride in me will be my happiness and glory. For men's love is little to me since Athelwold taught me to think meanly of all men, except you that slew him. And you shall be free to follow your own mind and be ever strenuous and vigilant and run after kingly pleasures, pursuing deer and wolf and beautiful women all over the land. And I shall listen to the tales of your adventures and conquests with a smile like that of a mother who sees her child playing seriously with its dolls and toys, talking to and caressing them. And in return you shall give me my desire, which is power and splendour; for these I crave, to be first and greatest, to raise up and cast down, and in all our life I shall be your help and stay in ruling this realm, so that our names may be linked together and shine in the annals of England for all time.

When Edgar slew Athelwold his age was twenty-two, and before he was a year older he had married Elfrida, to the rage of that great man and primate and more than premier, who, under Edgar, virtually

ruled England. And in his rage, and remembering
how he had dealt with a previous boy king, whose
beautiful young wife he had hounded to her dreadful
end, he charged Elfrida with having instigated her
husband's murder, and commanded the king to put
that woman away. This roused the man and passionate lover, and the tiger in the man, in Edgar, and
the wise and subtle-minded ecclesiastic quickly
recognised that he had set himself against one of a
will more powerful and dangerous than his own.
He remembered that it was Edgar, who, when he
had been deprived of his abbey and driven in
disgrace from the land, had recalled and made him
so great, and he knew that the result of a quarrel
between them would be a mighty upheaval in the
land and the sweeping away of all his great reforms.
And so, cursing the woman in his heart and secretly
vowing vengeance on her, he was compelled in the
interests of the Church to acquiesce in this fresh
crime of the king.

VII

EIGHT years had passed since the king's marriage with Elfrida, and the one child born to them was now seven, the darling of his parents, Ethelred the angelic child, who to the end of his long life would be praised for one thing only—his personal beauty. But Edward, his half-brother, now in his thirteenth year, was regarded by her with an almost equal affection, on account of his beauty and charm, his devotion to his stepmother, the only mother he had known, and, above all, for his love of his little half-brother. He was never happy unless he was with him, acting the part of guide and instructor as well as playfellow.

Edgar had recently completed one of his great works, the building of Corfe Castle, and now whenever he was in Wessex preferred it as a residence, since he loved best that part of England with its wide moors and hunting forests, and its neighbourhood to the sea and to Portland and Poole water. He had been absent for many weeks on a journey to Northumbria, and the last tidings of his movements were that he was on his way to the south, travelling on the Welsh border, and intended visiting the Abbot of Glastonbury before returning to Dorset. This religious house was already very great in his day; he had conferred many benefits on it, and contemplated still others.

It was summer time, a season of great heats, and Elfrida with the two little princes often went to the coast to spend a whole day in the open air by the sea. Her favourite spot was at the foot of a vast chalk down with a slight strip of woodland between its lowest slope and the beach. She was at this spot one day about noon where the trees were few and large, growing wide apart, and had settled herself on a pile of cushions placed at the roots of a big old oak tree, where from her seat she could look out over the blue expanse of water. But the hamlet and church close by on her left hand were hidden by the wood, though sounds issuing from it could be heard occasionally—shouts and bursts of laughter, and at times the music of a stringed instrument and a voice singing. These sounds came from her armed guard and other attendants who were speeding the idle hours of waiting in their own way, in eating and drinking and in games and dancing. Only two women remained to attend to her wants, and one armed man to keep watch and guard over the two boys at their play.

They were not now far off, not above fifty yards, among the big trees; but for hours past they had been away out of her sight, racing on their ponies over the great down; then bathing in the sea, Edward teaching his little brother to swim; then he had given him lessons in tree-climbing, and now, tired of all these exertions, and for variety's sake, they were amusing themselves by standing on their heads. Little Ethelred had tried and failed repeatedly, then at last, with hands and head firmly planted on the sward, he had succeeded in throwing his legs up and keeping them in a vertical position for a few seconds, this feat being loudly applauded by his young instructor.

Elfrida, who had witnessed this display from her seat, burst out laughing, then said to herself: O how I love these two beautiful boys almost with an equal love, albeit one is not mine! But Edward must be ever dear to me because of his sweetness and his love of me and, even more, his love and tender care of my darling. Yet am I not wholly free from an anxious thought of the distant future. Ah, no, let me not think of such a thing! This sweet child of a boy-father and girl-mother—the frail mother that died in her teens—he can never grow to be a proud, masterful, ambitious man—never aspire to wear his father's crown! Edgar's first-born, it is true, but not mine, and he can never be king. For Edgar and I are one; is it conceivable that he should oppose me in this—that we that are one in mind and soul shall at the last be divided and at enmity? Have we not said it an hundred times that we are one? One in all things except in passion. Yet this very coldness in me in which I differ from others is my chief strength and glory, and has made our two lives one life. And when he is tired and satiated with the common beauty and the common passions of other women he returns to me only to have his first love kindled afresh, and

when in love and pity I give myself to him and am
his bride afresh as when first he had my body in his
arms, it is to him as if one of the immortals had
stooped to a mortal, and he tells me I am the flower
of womankind and of the world, that my white body
is a perfect white flower, my hair a shining gold
flower, my mouth a fragrant scarlet flower, and my
eyes a sacred blue flower, surpassing all others in
loveliness. And when I have satisfied him, and the
tempest in his blood has abated, then for the rapture
he has had I have mine, when, ashamed at his
violence, as if it had been an insult to me, he covers his
face with my hair and sheds tears of love and
contrition on my breasts. O nothing can ever disunite
us! Even from the first, before I ever saw him,
when he was coming to me I knew that we were
destined to be one. And he too knew it from the
moment of seeing me, and knew that I knew it; and
when he sat at meat with us and looked smilingly
at the friend of his bosom and spoke merrily to him,
and resolved at the same time to take his life, he
knew that by so doing he would fulfil my desire, and
as my knowledge of the betrayal was first, so the
desire to shed that abhorred blood was in me first.
Nevertheless, I cannot be free of all anxious thoughts,
and fear too of my implacable enemy and traducer
who from a distance watches all my movements,
who reads Edgar's mind even as he would a book,
and what he finds there writ by me he seeks to blot
out; and thus does he ever thwart me. But though
I cannot measure my strength against his, it will

not always be so, seeing that he is old and I am young, with Time and Death on my side, who will like good and faithful servants bring him to the dust, so that my triumph must come. And when he is no more I shall have time to unbuild the structure he has raised with lies for stones and my name coupled with some evil deed cut in every stone. For I look ever to the future, even to the end to see this Edgar, with the light of life shining so brightly in him now, a venerable king with silver hair, his passions cool, his strength failing, leaning more heavily on me; until at last, persuaded by me, he will step down from the throne and resign his crown to our son—our Ethelred. And in him and his son after him, and in his son's sons we shall live still in their blood, and with them rule this kingdom of Edgar the Peaceful—a realm of everlasting peace.

Thus she mused, until overcome by her swift, crowding thoughts and passions, love and hate, with memories dreadful or beautiful, of her past and strivings of her mind to pierce the future, she burst into a violent storm of tears so that her frame was shaken, and covering her eyes with her hands she strove to get the better of her agitation lest her weakness should be witnessed by her attendants. But when this tempest had left her and she lifted her eyes again, it seemed to her that the burning tears which had relieved her heart had also washed away some trouble that had been like a dimness on all visible nature, and earth and sea and sky were glorified as if the sunlight flooding the world fell direct from the heavenly throne, and she sat drinking in pure delight from the sight of it and the soft, warm air she breathed.

Then, to complete her happiness, the silence that reigned around her was broken by a sweet, musical sound of a little bird that sang from the tree-top high above her head. This was the redstart, and the tree under which she sat was its singing-tree, to which it resorted many times a day to spend half an hour or so repeating its brief song at intervals of a few seconds—a small song that was like the song of the redbreast, subdued, refined and spiritualised, as of a spirit that lived within the tree.

Listening to it in that happy, tender mood which had followed her tears, she gazed up and tried to catch sight of it, but could see nothing but the deep-cut, green, translucent, clustering oak leaves showing the blue of heaven and shining like emeralds in the sunlight. O sweet, blessed little bird, she said, are you indeed a bird? I think you are a messenger sent to assure me that all my hopes and dreams of the distant days to come will be fulfilled. Sing again and again and again; I could listen for hours to that selfsame song.

But she heard it no more; the bird had flown away. Then, still listening, she caught a different sound—the loud hoof-beats of horses being ridden at furious speed towards the hamlet. Listening intently to that sound she heard, on its arrival at the hamlet, a sudden, great cry as if all the men gathered there had united their voices in one cry;

D

and she stood up, and her women came to her, and all together stood silently gazing in that direction. Then the two boys who had been lying on the turf not far off came running to them and caught her by the hands, one on each side, and Edward, looking up at her white, still face, cried, Mother, what is it you fear? But she answered no word. Then again the sound of hoofs was heard and they knew the riders were now coming at a swift gallop to them. And in a few moments they appeared among the trees, and reining up their horses at a distance of some yards, one sprang to the ground, and advancing to the queen, made his obeisance, then told her he had been sent to inform her of Edgar's death. He had been seized by a sudden violent fever in Gloucestershire, on his way to Glastonbury, and had died after two days' illness. He had been unconscious all the time, but more than once he had cried out, On to Glastonbury! and now in obedience to that command his body was being conveyed thither for interment at the abbey.

VIII

SHE had no tears to shed, no word to say, nor was there any sense of grief at her loss. She had loved him—once upon a time; she had always admired him for his better qualities; even his excessive pride and ostentation had been pleasing to her; finally she had been more than tolerant of his vices or weaknesses, regarding them as matters beneath her attention. Nevertheless, in their eight years of married life they had become increasingly repugnant to her stronger and colder nature. He had degenerated, bodily and mentally, and was not now like that shining one who had come to her at Wherwell Castle, who had not hesitated to strike the blow that had set her free. The tidings of his death had all at once sprung the truth on her mind that the old love was dead, that it had indeed been long dead, and that she had actually come to despise him.

But what should she do—what be—without him! She had been his queen, loved to adoration, and he had been her shield; now she was alone, face to face with her bitter, powerful enemy. Now it seemed to her that she had been living in a beautiful peaceful land, a paradise of fruit and flowers and all delightful things; that in a moment, as by a miracle, it had turned to a waste of black ashes still hot and smoking from the desolating flames that had passed over it. But she was not one to give herself over to despondency so long as there was anything to be done. Very quickly she roused herself to action, and dispatched messengers to all those powerful friends who shared her hatred of the great arch-bishop, and would be glad of the opportunity now offered of wresting the rule from his hands. Until now he had triumphed because he had had the king to support him even in his most arbitrary and tyrannical measures; now was the time to show a bold front, to proclaim her son as the right successor, and with herself, assisted by chosen coun-cillors to direct her boy, the power would be in her hands, and once more, as in King Edwin's day, the great Dunstan, disgraced and denounced, would be compelled to fly from the country lest a more dreadful punishment should befall him. Finally, leaving the two little princes at Corfe Castle, she travelled to Mercia to be with and animate her powerful friends and fellow-plotters with her presence.

All their plottings and movements were known to Dunstan, and he was too quick for them. Whilst they, divided among themselves, were debating and arranging their plans, he had called together all the leading bishops and councillors of the late king, and they had agreed that Edward must be proclaimed as the first-born; and although but a boy of thirteen, the danger to the country would not be so great as it would to give the succession to a child of seven years. Accordingly Edward was proclaimed

king and removed from Corfe Castle while the queen
was still absent in Mercia.

For a while it looked as if this bold and prompt
act on the part of Dunstan would have led to civil
war; but a great majority of the nobles gave their
adhesion to Edward, and Elfrida's friends soon
concluded that they were not strong enough to set
her boy up and try to overthrow Edward, or to
divide England again between two boy kings as
in Edwin and Edgar's early years.

She accordingly returned discomfited to Corfe Castle
and to her child, now always crying for his beloved
brother who had been taken from him; and there
was not in all England a more miserable woman
than Elfrida the queen. For after this defeat she
could hope no more; her power was gone past
recovery—all that had made her life beautiful and
glorious was gone. Now Corfe Castle was like that
other castle at Wherwell, where Earl Athelwold had
kept her like a caged bird for his pleasure when he
visited her; only worse, since she was eight years
younger then, her beauty fresher, her heart burning
with secret hopes and ambitions, and the great world
where there were towns and a king, and many noble
men and women gathered round him yet to be known.
And all these things had come to her and were now
lost—now nothing was left but bitterest regrets
and hatred of all those who had failed her at the
last. Hatred first of all and above all of her great
triumphant enemy, and hatred of the boy king
she had loved with a mother's love until now, and

cherished for many years. Hatred too of herself
when she recalled the part she had recently played
in Mercia, where she had not disdained to practise
all her fascinating arts on many persons she despised
in order to bind them to her cause, and had thereby
given cause to her monkish enemy to charge her
with immodesty. It was with something like hatred
too that she regarded her own child when he would
come crying to her, begging her to take him to his
beloved brother; carried away with sudden rage,
she would strike and thrust him violently from
her, then order her women to take him away and
keep him out of her sight.

Three years had gone by, during which she had
continued living alone at Corfe Castle, still under a
cloud and nursing her bitter revengeful feeling in her
heart, until that fatal afternoon on the eighteenth
day of March, 978.

The young king, now in his seventeenth year,
had come to these favourite hunting-grounds of
his late father, and was out hunting on that day.
He had lost sight of his companions in a wood or
thicket of thorn and furze, and galloping in search
of them he came out from the wood on the further
side; and there before him, not a mile away, was
Corfe Castle, his old beloved home, and the home
still of the two beings he loved best in the world
—his stepmother and his little half-brother. And
although he had been sternly warned that they
were his secret enemies, that it would be dangerous
to hold any intercourse with them, the sight of the

castle and his craving to look again on their dear faces overcame his scruples. There would be no harm, no danger to him and no great disobedience on his part to ride to the gates and see and greet them without dismounting.

When Elfrida was told that Edward himself was at the gates calling to her and Ethelred to come out to him she became violently excited, and cried out that God himself was on her side, and had delivered the boy into her hands. She ordered her servants to go out and persuade him to come in to her, to take away his horse as soon as he had dismounted, and not to allow him to leave the castle. Then, when they returned to say the king refused to dismount and again begged them to go to him, she went to the gates, but without the boy, and greeted him joyfully, while he, glad at the meeting, bent down and embraced her and kissed her face. But when she refused to send for Ethelred, and urged him persistently to dismount and come in to see his little brother who was crying for him, he began to notice the extreme excitement which burned in her eyes and made her voice tremble, and beginning to fear some design against him, he refused again more firmly to obey her wish; then she, to gain time, sent for wine for him to drink before parting from her. And during all this time while his departure was being delayed, her people, men and women, had been coming out until, sitting on his horse, he was in the midst of a crowd, and these too all looked on him with excited faces, which increased his apprehension, so that when he had drunk the wine he all at once set spurs to his horse to break away from among them. Then she, looking at her men, cried out: " Is this the way you serve me?" And no sooner had the words fallen from her lips than one man bounded forward, like a hound on its quarry, and coming abreast of the horse, dealt the king a blow with his knife in the side. The next moment the horse and rider were free of the crowd and rushing away over the moor. A cry of horror had burst from the women gathered there when the blow was struck; now all were silent, watching with white, scared faces as he rode swiftly away. Then presently they saw him swerve on his horse, then fall, with his right foot still remaining caught in the stirrup, and that the panic-stricken horse was dragging him at furious speed over the rough moor.

Only then the queen spoke, and in an agitated voice told them to mount and follow; and charged them that if they overtook the horse and found that the king had been killed, to bury the body where it would not be found, so that the manner of his death should not be known.

When the men returned they reported that they had found the dead body of the king a mile away, where the horse had got free of it, and they had buried it in a thicket where it would never be discovered.

IX

WHEN Edward in sudden terror set spurs to his horse: when at the same moment a knife flashed out and the fatal blow was delivered, Elfrida too, like the other women witnesses in the crowd, had uttered a cry of horror. But once the deed was accomplished and the assurance received that the body had been hidden where it would never be found, the feeling experienced at the spectacle was changed to one of exultation. For now at last, after three miserable years of brooding on her defeat, she had unexpectedly triumphed, and it was as if she already had her foot set on her enemies' necks. For now her boy would be king—happily there was no other candidate in the field; now her great friends from all over the land would fly to her aid, and with them for her councillors she would practically be the ruler during the king's long minority.

Thus she exulted; then, when that first tempest of passionate excitement had abated, came a revulsion of feeling when the vivid recollections of that pitiful scene returned and would not be thrust away; when she saw again the change from affection and delight at beholding her to suspicion and fear, then terror, come into the face of the boy she had loved; when she witnessed the dreadful blow and watched him when he swerved and fell from the

saddle and the frightened horse galloped wildly
away dragging him over the rough moor. For now
she knew that in her heart she had never hated
him: the animosity had been only on the surface
and was an overflow of her consuming hatred of
the primate. She had always loved the boy, and
now that he no longer stood in her way to power
she loved him again. And she had slain him! O no,
she was thankful to think she had not! His death
had come about by chance. Her commands to her
people had been that he was not to be allowed to
leave the castle; she had resolved to detain him,
to hide and hold him a captive, to persuade or in
some way compel him to abdicate in his brother's
favour. She could not now say just how she had
intended to deal with him, but it was never her
intention to murder him. Her commands had been
misunderstood, and she could not be blamed for
his death, however much she was to benefit by it.
God would not hold her accountable.

Could she then believe that she was guiltless in
God's sight? Alas! on second thoughts she dared
not affirm it. She was guiltless only in the way
that she had been guiltless of Athelwold's murder;
had she not rejoiced at the part she had had in that
act? Athelwold had deserved his fate, and she had
never repented that deed, nor had Edgar. She
had not dealt the fatal blow then nor now, but
she had wished for Edward's death even as she had
wished for Athelwold's, and it was for her the
blow was struck. It was a difficult and dreadful

question. She was not equal to it. Let it be put off, the pressing question now was, what would man's judgment be — how would she now stand before the world?

And now the hope came that the secret of the king's disappearance would never be known; that after a time it would be assumed that he was dead, and that his death would never be traced to her door.

A vain hope, as she quickly found! There had been too many witnesses of the deed both of the castle people and those who lived outside the gates. The news spread fast and far as if carried by winged messengers, so that it was soon known throughout the kingdom, and everywhere it was told and believed that the queen herself had dealt the fatal blow.

Not Elfrida nor anyone living at that time could have foretold the effect on the people generally of this deed, described as the foulest which had been done in Saxon times. There had in fact been a thousand blacker deeds in the England of that dreadful period, but never one that touched the heart and imagination of the whole people in the same way. Furthermore, it came after a long pause, a serene interval of many years in the everlasting turmoil—the years of the reign of Edgar the Peaceful, whose early death had up till then been its one great sorrow. A time too of recovery from a state of insensibility to evil deeds; of increasing civilisation and the softening of hearts. For Edward was the child of Edgar and his child-wife, who was beautiful and beloved and died young; and he had inherited the beauty, charm, and all engaging qualities of his parents. It is true that these qualities were known at first-hand only by those who were about him; but from these the feeling inspired had been communicated to those outside in ever-widening circles until it was spread over all the land, so that there was no habitation, from the castle to the hovel, in which the name of Edward was not as music on men's lips. And we of the present generation can perhaps understand this better than those of any other in the past centuries, for having a prince and heir to the English throne of this same name so great in our annals, one as universally loved as was Edward the Second, afterwards called the Martyr, in his day.

One result of this general outburst of feeling was that all those who had been, openly or secretly, in alliance with Elfrida now hastened to dissociate themselves from her. She was told that by her own rash act in killing the king before the world she had ruined her own cause for ever.

And Dunstan was not defeated after all. He made haste to proclaim the son, the boy of ten years, king of England, and at the same time to denounce the mother as a murderess. Nor did she dare to resist him when he removed the little prince from Corfe Castle and placed him with some of his own creatures, with monks for schoolmasters and guardians, whose first lesson to him would be detestation of his mother. This lesson too had to be impressed on the public mind; and at once, in obedience to

this command, every preaching monk in every chapel
in the land raged against the queen, the enemy of
the archbishop and of religion, the tigress in human
shape, and author of the greatest crime known in
the land since Cerdic's landing. No fortitude could
stand against such a storm of execration. It over-
whelmed her. It was, she believed, a preparation
for the dreadful doom about to fall on her. This
was her great enemy's day, and he would no longer
be baulked of his revenge. She remembered that
Edwin had died by the assassin's hand, and the awful
fate of his queen Elgitha, whose too beautiful face
was branded with hot irons, and who was ham-
strung and left to perish in unimaginable agony. She
was like the hunted roe-deer hiding in a close
thicket and listening, trembling, to the hunters
shouting and blowing on their horns and to the
baying of their dogs, seeking for her in the wood.

Could she defend herself against them in her
castle? She consulted her guard as to this, with the
result that most of the men secretly left her. There
was nothing for her to do but wait in dreadful
suspense, and thereafter she would spend many hours
every day in a tower commanding a wide view of
the surrounding level country to watch the road
with anxious eyes. But the feared hunters came not;
the sound of the cry for vengeance grew fainter and
fainter until it died into silence. It was at length
borne in on her that she was not to be punished—
at all events, not here and by man. It came as a
surprise to everyone, herself included. But it had

been remembered that she was Edgar's widow and
the king's mother, and that her power and influence
were dead. Never again would she lift her head in
England. Furthermore, Dunstan was growing old;
and albeit his zeal for religion, pure and undefiled
as he understood it, was not abated, the cruel, ruth-
less instincts and temper, which had accompanied
and made it effective in the great day of conflict
when he was engaged in sweeping from England the
sin and scandal of a married clergy, had by now burnt
themselves out. Vengeance is mine, saith the Lord,
I will repay, and he was satisfied to have no more
to do with her. Let the abhorred woman answer
to God for her crimes.

But now that all fear of punishment by man was
over, this dreadful thought that she was answerable
to God weighed more and more heavily on her. Nor
could she escape by day or night from the persistent
image of the murdered boy. It haunted her like
a ghost in every room, and when she climbed to a
tower to look out it was to see his horse rushing
madly away dragging his bleeding body over the
moor. Or when she went out to the gate it was still
to find him there, sitting on his horse, his face lighting
up with love and joy at beholding her again; then
the change—the surprise, the fear, the wine-cup, the
attempt to break away, her cry—the unconsidered
words she had uttered—and the fatal blow! The
cry that rose from all England calling on God to
destroy her! would that be her torment—would it
sound in her ears through all eternity?

Corfe Castle became unendurable to her, and eventually she moved to Bere, in Dorset, where the lands were her property and she possessed a house of her own, and there for upwards of a year she resided in the strictest seclusion.

It then came out and was quickly noised abroad that the king's body had been discovered long ago—miraculously it was said—in that brake near Corfe Castle where it had been hidden; that it had been removed to and secretly buried at Wareham, and it was also said that miracles were occurring at that spot. This caused a fresh outburst of excitement in the country; the cry of miracles roused the religious houses all over Wessex, and there was a clamour for possession of the remains. This was a question for the heads of the Church to decide, and it was eventually decreed that the monastery of Shaftesbury, founded by King Alfred, Edward's great-great-grandfather, should have the body. Shaftesbury then, in order to advertise so important an acquisition to the world, resolved to make the removal of the remains the occasion of a great ceremony, a magnificent procession bearing the sacred remains from Wareham to the distant little city on the hill, attended by representatives from religious houses all over the country and by the pious generally.

Elfrida, sitting alone in her house, brooding on her desolation, heard of all these happenings and doings with increasing excitement; then all at once resolved to take part herself in the procession. This was seemingly a strange, almost incredible departure for one of her indomitable character and so embittered against the primate, even as he was against her. But her fight with him was now ended; she was defeated, broken, deprived of everything that she valued in life; it was time to think about the life to come. Furthermore, it now came to her that this was not her own thought, but that it had been whispered to her soul by some compassionate being of a higher order, and it was suggested to her that here was an opportunity for a first step towards a reconciliation with God and man. She dared not disregard it. Once more she would appear before the world, not as the beautiful, magnificent Elfrida, the proud and powerful woman of other days, but as a humble penitent doing her bitter penance in public, one of a thousand or ten thousand humble pilgrims, clad in mean garments, riding only when overcome with fatigue, and at the last stage of that long twenty-five-mile journey casting off her shoes to climb the steep stony road on naked, bleeding feet.

This resolution, in which she was strongly supported by the local priesthood, had a mollifying effect on the people, and something like compassion began to mingle with their feelings of hatred towards her. But when it was reported to Dunstan, he fell into a rage, and imagined or pretended to believe that some sinister design was hidden under it. She was the same woman, he said, who had instigated the murder of her first husband by means of a trick of this kind. She must not be allowed to show her face again. He then dispatched a stern and threatening message forbidding her to take any part in or show herself at the procession.

This came at the last moment when all her preparations had been made; but she dared not disobey. The effect was to increase her misery. It was as if the gates of mercy and deliverance, which had been opened, miraculously as she believed, had now been once more closed against her; and it was also as if her enemy had said: I have spared you the branding with hot irons and slashing of sinews with sharp knives, not out of compassion, but in order to subject you to a more terrible punishment.

Despair possessed her, which turned to sullen rage when she found that the feeling of the people around her had again become hostile, owing to the report that her non-appearance at the procession was due to the discovery by Dunstan in good time of a secret plot against the State on her part. Her house at Bere became unendurable to her; she resolved to quit it, and made choice of Salisbury as her next place of residence. It was not far to go, and she had a good house there which had not been used since Edgar's death, but was always kept ready for her occupation.

E

X

IT was about the middle of the afternoon when Elfrida on horseback and attended by her mounted guard of twenty or more men, followed by a convoy of carts with her servants and luggage, arrived at Salisbury, and was surprised and disturbed at the sight of a vast concourse of people standing without the gates.

It had got abroad that she was coming to Salisbury on that day, and it was also now known throughout Wessex that she had not been allowed to attend the procession to Shaftesbury. This had excited the people, and a large part of the inhabitants of the town and the adjacent hamlets had congregated to witness her arrival.

On her approach the crowd opened out on either side to make way for her and her men, and glancing to this side and that she saw that every pair of eyes in all that vast silent crowd were fixed intently on her face.

Then came a fresh surprise when she found a mounted guard standing with drawn swords before the gates. The captain of the guard, lifting his hand, cried out to her to halt, then in a loud voice he informed her he had been ordered to turn her back from the gates. Was it then to witness this fresh insult that the people had now been brought together?

Anger and apprehension struggled for mastery in
her breast and choked her utterance when she
attempted to speak. She could only turn to her
men, and in instant response to her look they drew
their swords and pressed forward as if about to
force their way in. This movement on their part was
greeted with a loud burst of derisive laughter from
the town guard. Then from out of the middle of the
crowd of lookers-on came a cry of "Murderess!"
quickly followed by another shout of "Go back,
murderess, you are not wanted here!" This was a
signal for all the unruly spirits in the throng—all
those whose delight is to trample upon the fallen—and
from all sides there arose a storm of jeers and exe-
crations, and it was as if she was in the midst of a
frantic bellowing herd eager to gore and trample her
to death. And these were the same people that a few
short years ago would rush out from their houses
to gaze with pride and delight at her, their beautiful
queen, and applaud her to the echo whenever she
appeared at their gates! Now, better than ever
before, she realised the change of feeling towards
her from affectionate loyalty to abhorrence, and
drained to the last bitterest dregs the cup of shame
and humiliation.

With trembling hand she turned her horse round,
and bending her ashen white face low rode slowly
out of the crowd, her men close to her on either
side, threatening with their swords those that pressed
nearest and followed in their retreat by shouts and
jeers. But when well out of sight and sound of the

people she dismounted and sat down on the turf to rest and consider what was to be done. By-and-by a mounted man was seen coming from Salisbury at a fast gallop. He came with a letter and message to the queen from an aged nobleman, one she had known in former years at court. He informed her that he owned a large house at or near Amesbury which he could not now use on account of his age and infirmities, which compelled him to remain in Salisbury. This house she might occupy for as long as she wished to remain in the neighbourhood. He had received permission from the governor of the town to offer it to her, and the only condition was that she must not return to Salisbury.

There was thus one friend left to the reviled and outcast queen—this aged dying man!

Once more she set forth with the messenger as guide, and about set of sun arrived at the house, which was to be her home for the next two to three years, in this darkest period of her life. Yet she could not have found a habitation and surroundings more perfectly suited to her wants and the mood she was in. The house, which was large enough to accommodate all her people, was on the west side of the Avon, a quarter of a mile below Amesbury and two to three hundred yards distant from the river bank, and was surrounded by enclosed land with gardens and orchards, the river itself forming the boundary on one side. Here was the perfect seclusion she desired: here she could spend her hours and days as she ever loved to do in the open

air without sight of any human countenance excepting those of her own people, since now strange faces
had become hateful to her. Then, again, she loved
riding, and just outside of her gates was the great
green expanse of the Downs, where she could spend
hours on horseback without meeting or seeing a
human figure except occasionally a solitary shepherd
guarding his flock. So great was the attraction the
Downs had for her, she herself marvelled at it. It
was not merely the sense of power and freedom the
rider feels on a horse with the exhilarating effect
of swift motion and a wide horizon. Here she had
got out of the old and into a new world better suited
to her changed spirit. For in that world of men
and women in which she had lived until now all
nature had become interfused with her own and
other people's lives—passions and hopes and fears
and dreams and ambitions. Now it was as if an
obscuring purple mist had been blown away, leaving
the prospect sharp and clear to her sight as it had
never appeared before. A wide prospect, whose
grateful silence was only broken by the cry or song
of some wild bird. Great thickets of dwarf thorn
tree and brambles and gorse, aflame with yellow
flowers or dark to blackness by contrast with the
pale verdure of the earth. And open reaches of
elastic turf, its green suffused or sprinkled with
red or blue or yellow, according to the kind of flowers
proper to the season and place. The sight, too, of
wild creatures: fallow-deer, looking yellow in the
distance when seen amid the black gorse; a flock

of bustards taking to flight on her approach would rush away, their spread wings flashing silver-white in the brilliant sunshine. She was like them on her horse, borne swiftly as on wings above the earth, but always near it. Then, casting her eyes up, she would watch the soarers, the buzzards, or harriers and others, circling up from earth on broad motionless wings, bird above bird, ever rising and diminishing to fade away at last into the universal blue. Then, as if aspiring too, she would seek the highest point on some high down, and sitting on her horse survey the prospect before her—the sea of rounded hills, hills beyond hills, stretching away to the dim horizon, and over it all the vast blue dome of heaven. Sky and earth, with thorny brakes and grass and flowers and wild creatures, with birds that flew low and others soaring up into heaven—what was the secret meaning it had for her? She was like one groping for a key in a dark place. Not a human figure visible, not a sign of human occupancy on that expanse! Was this then the secret of her elation? The all-powerful, dreadful God she was at enmity with, whom she feared and fled from, was not here. He, or his spirit, was where man inhabited, in cities and other centres of population, where there were churches and monasteries.

To think this was a veritable relief to her. God was where men worshipped him, and not here! She hugged the new belief and it made her bold and defiant. " Doubtless, if he is here," she would say, " and can read my thoughts, my horse in his very next

gallop will put his foot in a mole-run, and bring
me down and break my neck. Or when yon black
cloud comes over me, if it is a thunder-cloud, the
lightning out of it will strike me dead. If he will
but listen to his servant Dunstan this will surely
happen. Was it God or the head shepherd of his
sheep, here in England, who, when I tried to enter
the fold, beat me off with his staff and set his dogs
on me so that I was driven away, torn and bleeding,
to hide myself in a solitary place? Would it then
be better for me to go with my cries for mercy to
his seat? O no, I could not come to him there; his
doorkeepers would bar the way, and perhaps bring
together a crowd of their people to howl at me—
'Go away, Murderess, you are not wanted here!'"

Now in spite of those moments, or even hours,
of elation, during which her mind would recover
its old independence until the sense of freedom was
like an intoxication; when she cried out against
God that he was cruel and unjust in his dealings
with his creatures, that he had raised up and given
power to the man who held the rod over her, one
who in God's holy name had committed crimes
infinitely greater than hers, and she refused to
submit to him—in spite of it all she could never shake
off the terrible thought that in the end, at God's
judgment seat, she would have to answer for her
own dark deeds. She could not be free of her religion.
She was like one who tears a written paper to pieces
and scatters the pieces in anger to see them blown
away like snowflakes on the wind ; who by-and-by

discovers one small fragment clinging to his garments, and looking at the half a dozen words and half-words appearing on it, adds others from memory or of his own invention. So she, with what was left when she thrust her religion away, built for herself a different one which was yet like the old; and even here in this solitude she was able to find a house and sacred place for meditation and prayer, in which she prayed indirectly to the God she was at enmity with. For now invariably on returning from her ride to her house at Amesbury she would pay a visit to the Great Stones, the ancient temple of Stonehenge. Dismounting, she would order her attendants to take her horse away and wait for her at a distance, so as not to be disturbed by the sound of their talking. Going in she would seat herself on the central or altar stone and give a little time to meditation—to the tuning of her mind. That circle of roughhewn stones, rough with grey lichen, were the pillars of her cathedral, with the infinite blue sky for roof, and for incense the smell of flowers and aromatic herbs, and for music the far-off faintly heard sounds that came to her from the surrounding wilderness—the tremulous bleating of sheep and the sudden wild cry of hawk or stone curlew. Closing her eyes she would summon the familiar image and vision of the murdered boy, always coming so quickly, so vividly, that she had brought herself to believe that it was not a mere creation of her own mind and of remorse, a memory, but that he was actually there with her. Moving her hand over the rough stone she would by-and-by let it rest, pressing it on the stone, and would say: "Now I have your hand in mine, and am looking with my soul's eyes into yours, listen again to the words I have spoken so many times. You would not be here if you did not remember me and pity and even love me still. Know then that I am now alone in the world, that I am hated by the world because of your bitter death. And there is not now one living being in the world that I love, for I have ceased to love even my own boy, your old beloved playmate, seeing that he has long been taken from me and taught with all others to despise and hate me. And of all those who inhabit the regions above, in all that innumerable multitude of angels and saints, and of all who have died on earth and been forgiven, you alone have any feeling of compassion for me and can intercede for me. Plead for me—plead for me, O my son; for who is there in heaven or earth that can plead so powerfully for me that are stained with your blood!"

Then, having finished her prayer, and wiped away all trace of tears and painful emotions, she would summon her attendants and ride home, in appearance and bearing still the Elfrida of her great days —the calm, proud-faced, beautiful woman who was once Edgar's queen.

THE time had arrived when Elfrida was deprived of this her one relief and consolation —her rides on the Downs and the exercise of her religion at the temple of the Great Stones —when in the second winter of her residence at Amesbury there fell a greater darkness than that of winter on England, when the pirate kings of the north began once more to frequent our shores, and the daily dreadful tale of battles and massacres and burning of villages and monasteries was heard throughout the kingdom. These invasions were at first confined to the eastern counties, but the agitation, with movements of men and outbreaks of lawlessness, were everywhere in the country, and the queen was warned that it was no longer safe for her to go out on Salisbury Plain.

The close seclusion in which she had now to live, confined to house and enclosed land, affected her spirits, and this was her darkest period, and it was also the turning-point in her life. For I now come to the strange story of her maid Editha, who, despite her humble position in the house, and albeit she was but a young girl in years, one, moreover, of a meek, timid disposition, was yet destined to play an exceedingly important part in the queen's history.

It happened that by chance or design the queen's

maid, who was her closest attendant, who dressed and undressed her, was suddenly called away on some urgent matter, and this girl Editha, a stranger to all, was put in her place. The queen, who was in a moody and irritable state, presently discovered that the sight and presence of this girl produced a soothing effect on her darkened mind. She began to notice her when the maid combed her hair, when sitting with half-closed eyes in profound dejection she first looked attentively at that face behind her head in the mirror and marvelled at its fairness, the perfection of its lines and its delicate colouring, the pale gold hair and strangely serious grey eyes that were never lifted to meet her own.

What was it in this face, she asked herself, that held her and gave some rest to her tormented spirit? It reminded her of that crystal stream of sweet and bitter memories, at Wherwell, on which she used to gaze and in which she used to dip her hands, then to press the wetted hands to her lips. It also reminded her of an early morning sky, seen beyond and above the green dew-wet earth, so infinitely far away, so peaceful with a peace that was not of this earth.

It was not then merely its beauty that made this face so much to her, but something greater behind it, some inner grace, the peace of God in her soul.

One day there came for the queen as a gift from some distant town a volume of parables and fables for her entertainment. It was beautiful to the sight, being richly bound in silk and gold embroidery; but on opening it she soon found that there was little pleasure to be got from it on account of the difficulty she found in reading the crabbed handwriting. After spending some minutes in trying to decipher a paragraph or two she threw the book in disgust on the floor.

The maid picked it up, and after a glance at the first page said it was easy to her, and she asked if the queen would allow her to read it to her.

Elfrida, surprised, asked how it came about that her maid was able to read so difficult a script with ease, or was able to read at all; and this was the first question she had condescended to put to the girl. Editha replied that she had been taught as a child by a great-uncle, a learned man; that she had been made to read volumes in a great variety of scripts to him, until reading had come easy to her, both Saxon and Latin.

Then, having received permission, she read the first fable aloud, and Elfrida listening, albeit without interest in the tale itself, found that the voice increased the girl's attraction for her. From that time the queen made her read to her every day. She would make her sit a little distance from her, and reclining on her couch, her head resting on her hand, she would let her eyes dwell on that sweet saint-like face until the reading was finished.

One day she read from the same book a tale of a great noble, an ealdorman who was ruler under the king of that part of the country where his possessions were, whose power was practically unlimited and his word law. But he was a wise and just man,

regardful of the rights of others, even of the meanest
of men, so that he was greatly reverenced and loved
by the people. Nevertheless, he too, like all men
in authority, both good and bad, had his enemies,
and the chief of these was a noble of a proud and
froward temper who had quarrelled with him about
their respective rights in certain properties where
their lands adjoined. Again and again it was shown
to him that his contention was wrong; the judgments
against him only served to increase his bitterness
and hostility until it seemed that there would never
be an end to that strife. This at length so incensed
his powerful overlord that he was forcibly deprived
of his possessions and driven out beggared from his
home. But no punishment, however severe, could
change his nature; it only roused him to greater
fury, a more fixed determination to have his revenge,
so that, outcast as he was, his enmity was still to
be feared and he was a danger to the ruler and the
community in general. Then, at last, the great earl
said he would suffer this state of things no longer,
and he ordered his men to go out and seek and take
him captive and bring him up for a final judgment.
This was done, and the ruler then said he would
not have him put to death as he was advised to do,
so as to be rid of him once for all, but would inflict
a greater punishment on him. He then made them
put heavy irons on his ankles, riveted so that they
should never be removed, and condemned him to
slavery and to labour every day in his fields and
pleasure-grounds for the rest of his life. To see his

hated enemy reduced to that condition would, he said, be a satisfaction to him whenever he walked in his gardens.

These stern commands were obeyed, and when the miserable man refused to do his task and cried out in a rage that he would rather die, he was scourged until the blood ran from the wounds made by the lash; and at last, to escape from this torture, he was compelled to obey, and from morning to night he laboured on the land, planting and digging and doing whatever there was to do, always watched by his overseer, his food thrown to him as to a dog; laughed and jeered at by the meanest of the servants.

After a certain time, when his body grew hardened so that he could labour all day without pain, and, being fatigued, sleep all night without waking, though he had nothing but straw on a stone floor to lie upon; and when he was no longer mocked or punished or threatened with the lash, he began to reflect more and more on his condition, and to think that it would be possible to him to make it more endurable. When brooding on it, when he repined and cursed, it then seemed to him worse than death; but when, occupied with his task, he forgot that he was the slave of his enemy, who had overcome and broken him, then it no longer seemed so heavy. The sun still shone for him as for others; the earth was as green, the sky as blue, the flowers as fragrant. This reflection made his misery less; and by-and-by it came into his mind that it would be lessened more and more if he could forget that his master was his enemy and cruel persecutor, who took delight in the thought of his sufferings; if he could imagine that he had a different master, a great and good man who had ever been kind to him and whom his sole desire was to please. This thought working in his mind began to give him a satisfaction in his toil, and this change in him was noticed by his taskmaster, who began to see that he did his work with an understanding so much above that of his fellows that all those who laboured with him were influenced by his example, and whatsoever the toil was in which he had a part the work was better done. From the taskmaster this change became known to the chief head of all the lands, who thereupon had him set to other more important tasks, so that at last he was not only a toiler with pick and spade and pruning-knife, but his counsel was sought in everything that concerned the larger works on the land; in forming plantations, in the draining of wet grounds and building of houses and bridges and the making of new roads. And in all these works he acquitted himself well.

Thus he laboured for years, and it all became known to the ruler, who at length ordered the man to be brought before him to receive yet another final judgment. And when he stood before him, hairy, dirty and unkempt, in his ragged raiment, with toil-hardened hands and heavy irons on his legs, he first ordered the irons to be removed.

The smiths came with their files and hammers, and with much labour took them off.

Then the ruler, his powerful old enemy, spoke these words to him: " I do not know what your motives were in doing what you have done all these years of your slavery; nor do I ask to be told. It is sufficient for me to know you have done these things, which are for my benefit and are a debt which must now be paid. You are henceforth free, and the possessions you were deprived of shall be restored to you, and as to the past and all the evil thoughts you had of me and all you did against me, it is forgiven and from this day will be forgotten. Go now in peace."

When this last word had been spoken by his enemy, all that remained of the old hatred and bitterness went out of him, and it was as if his soul as well as his feet had been burdened with heavy irons and that they had now been removed, and that he was free with a freedom he had never known before.

When the reading was finished, the queen with eyes cast down remained for some time immersed in thought; then with a keen glance at the maid's face she asked for the book, and opening it began slowly turning the leaves. By-and-by her face darkened, and in a stern tone of voice she said: " Come here and show me in this book the parable you have just read, and then you shall also show me two or three other parables you have read to me on former occasions, which I cannot find."

The maid, pale and trembling, came and dropped on her knees and begged forgiveness for having recited these three or four tales, which she had heard or read elsewhere and committed to memory, and had pretended to read them out of the book.

Then the queen in a sudden rage said: "Go from me and let me not see you again if you do not wish to be stripped and scourged and thrust naked out of the gates! And you only escape this punishment because the deceit you have been practising on me is, to my thinking, not of your own invention, but that of some crafty monk who is making you his instrument."

Editha, terrified and weeping, hurriedly quitted the room.

By-and-by, when that sudden tempest of rage had subsided, the despondence, which had been somewhat lightened by the maid's presence, came back on her so heavily that it was almost past endurance. She rose and went to her sleeping-room, and knelt before a table on which stood a crucifix with an image of the Saviour on it—the emblem of the religion she had so great a quarrel with. But not to pray. Folding her arms on the table and dropping her face on them she said: "What have I done?" And again and again she repeated: "What have I done? Was it indeed a monk who taught her this deceit, or some higher being who put it in her mind to whisper a hope to my soul? To show me a way of escape from everlasting death—to labour in his fields and pleasure-grounds, a wretched slave with irons on her feet, to be scourged and mocked at, and in this state to cast out hatred and bitterness

F

from my own soul and all remembrance of the injuries he had inflicted on me—to teach myself through long miserable years that this powerful enemy and persecutor is a kind and loving master? This is the parable, and now my soul tells me it would be a light punishment when I look at the red stains on these hands, and when the image of the boy I loved and murdered comes back to me. This then was the message, and I drove the messenger from me with cruel threats and insult."

Suddenly she rose, and going hurriedly out, called to her maids to bring Editha to her. They told her the maid had departed instantly on being dismissed, and had gone upwards of an hour. Then she ordered them to go and search for her in all the neighbourhood, at every house, and when they had found her to bring her back by persuasion or by force.

They returned after a time only to say they had sought for her everywhere and had failed to find or hear any report of her, but that some of the mounted men who had gone to look for her on the roads had not yet returned.

Left alone once more she turned to a window which looked towards Salisbury, and saw the westering sun hanging low in a sky of broken clouds over the valley of the Avon and the green downs on either side. And, still communing with herself, she said: " I know that I shall not endure it long—this great fear of God—I know that it will madden me. And for the unforgiven who die mad there can be no hope. Only the sight of my maid's face with God's peace on it could save me from madness. No, I shall not go mad! I shall take it as a sign that I cannot be forgiven if the sun goes down without my seeing her again. I shall kill myself before madness comes and rest oblivious of life and all things, even of God's wrath, until the dreadful waking."

For some time longer she continued standing motionless, watching the sun, now sinking behind a dark cloud, then emerging and lighting up the dim interior of her room and her stone-white, desolate face.

Then once more her servants came back, and with them Editha, who had been found on the road to Salisbury, half-way there.

Left alone together, the queen took the maid by the hand and led her to a seat then fell on her knees before her and clasped her legs and begged her forgiveness. When the maid replied that she had forgiven her, and tried to raise her up, she resisted, and cried: " No, I cannot rise from my knees nor loose my hold on you until I have confessed to you and you have promised to save me. Now I see in you not my maid who combs my hair and ties my shoe-strings, but one that God loves, whom He exalts above the queens and nobles of the earth, and while I cling to you He will not strike. Look into this heart that has hated Him, look at its frightful passions, its blood-guiltiness, and have compassion on me! And if you, O Editha, should reply to me that it is His will, for He has said it, that every soul shall save itself, show me the way. How shall I approach Him? Teach me humility!"

Thus she pleaded and abased herself. Nevertheless it was a hard task she imposed upon her helper, seeing that humility, of all virtues, was the most contrary to her nature. And when she was told that the first step to be taken was to be reconciled to the Church, and to the head of the Church, her chief enemy and persecutor, whose monks, obedient to his command, had blackened her name in all the land, her soul was in fierce revolt. Nevertheless she had to submit, seeing that God Himself through His Son when on earth and His Son's disciples had established the Church, and by that door only could any soul approach him. So there was an end to that conflict, and Elfrida, beaten and broken, although ever secretly hating the tonsured keepers of her soul, set forth under their guidance on her weary pilgrimage—the long last years of her bitter expiation.

Yet there was to be one more conflict between the two women—the imperious mistress and the humble-minded maid. This was when Editha announced to the other that the time had now come for her to depart. But the queen wished to keep her, and tried by all means to do so, by pleading with her and by threatening to detain her by force. Then repenting her anger and remembering the great debt of gratitude owing to the girl, she resolved to reward her generously, to bestow wealth on her, but in such a form that it would appear to the girl as a beautiful parting gift from one who had loved her: only afterwards, when they were far apart, would she discover its real value.

A memory of the past had come to her—of that day, sixteen years ago, when her lover came to her and using sweet flattering words poured out from a bag a great quantity of priceless jewels into her lap, and of the joy she had in the gift. Also how from the day of Athelwold's death she had kept those treasures put away in the same bag out of her sight. Nor in all the days of her life with Edgar had she ever worn a gem, though she had always loved to array herself magnificently, but her ornaments had been gold only, the work of the best artists in Europe. Now, in imitation of Athelwold, when his manner of bestowing the jewels had so charmed her, she would bestow them on the girl.

Accordingly, when the moment of separation came and Editha was made to seat herself, the queen standing over her with the bag in her hand said: "Do you, Editha, love all beautiful things?" And when the maid had replied that she did, the other said: "Then take these gems, which are beautiful, as a parting gift from me." And with that she poured out the mass of glittering jewels into the girl's lap.

But the maid, without touching or even looking at them, and with a cry: "I want no jewels!" started to her feet, so that they were all scattered upon the floor.

The queen stared astonished at the face before her with its new look of pride and excitement, then with rising anger she said: "Is my maid too proud, then, to accept a gift from me? Does she not know that a single one of those gems thrown on the floor would be more than a fortune to her?"

The girl replied in the same proud way: "I am not your maid, and gems are no more to me than pebbles from the brook!"

Then all at once recovering her meek, gentle manner she cried in a voice that pierced the queen's heart: "O, not your maid, only your fellow-worker in our Master's fields and pleasure-grounds! Before I ever beheld your face, and since we have been together, my heart has bled for you, and my daily cry to God has been: 'Forgive her! Forgive her, for His sake who died for our sins!' And this shall I continue to cry though I shall see you no more on earth. But we shall meet again. Not, O unhappy queen, at life's end, but long afterwards—long, long years! long ages!"

Dropping on her knees she caught and kissed the queen's hand, shedding abundant tears on it, then rose and was quickly gone.

Elfrida, left to herself, scarcely recovered from the shock of surprise at that sudden change in the girl's manner, began to wonder at her own blindness in not having seen through her disguise from the first. The revelation had come to her only at the last moment in that proud gesture and speech when her gift was rejected, not without scorn. A child of nobles great as any in the land, what had made her do this thing? What indeed but the heavenly spirit that was in her, the spirit that was in Christ —the divine passion to save!

Now she began to ponder on those last words the maid had spoken, and the more she thought of them the greater became her sadness, until it was like the approach of death. O terrible words! Yet it was what she had feared, even when she had dared to hope for forgiveness. Now she knew what her life after death was to be, since the word had been spoken by those inspired lips. O dreadful destiny! To dwell alone, to tread alone that desert desolate, that illimitable waste of burning sand stretching from star to star through infinite space, where was no rock nor tree to give her shade, no fountain to quench her fiery thirst! For that was how she imaged the future life, as a desert to be dwelt in until in the end, when in God's good time—the time of One to whom a thousand years are as one day—she would receive the final pardon and be admitted to rest in a green and shaded place.

Overcome with the agonising thought, she sank down on her couch and fell into a faint. In that state she was found by her women, reclining, still as death, with eyes closed, the whiteness of death in her face; and thinking her dead they rushed out terrified, crying aloud and lamenting that the queen was dead.

XII

SHE was not dead. She recovered from that swoon, but never from the deep, unbroken sadness caused by those last words of the maid Editha, which had overcome and nearly slain her. She now abandoned her seclusion, but the world she returned to was not the old one. The thought that every person she met was saying in his or her heart, "This is Elfrida; this is the queen who murdered Edward the Martyr, her stepson," made that world impossible. The men and women she now consorted with were the religious and ecclesiastics of all degrees, and abbots and abbesses. These were the people she loved least, yet now into their hands she deliberately gave herself; and to those who questioned her, to her spiritual guides, she revealed all her life and thoughts and passions, opening her soul to their eyes like a manuscript for them to read and consider; and when they told her that in God's sight she was guilty of the murder both of Edward and Athelwold, she replied that they doubtless knew best what was in God's mind, and whatever they commanded her to do, that should be done, and if in her own mind it was not as they said, this could be taken as a defect in her understanding. For in her heart she was not changed, and had not yet and never would learn the bitter lesson of humility.

Furthermore, she knew better than they what life and death had in store for her, since it had been revealed to her by holier lips than those of any priest. Lips on which had been laid a coal from the heavenly altar, and what they had foretold would come to pass—that unearthly pilgrimage and puri-fication—that destiny, dreadful, ineluctable, that made her soul faint to think of it. Here, on this earth, it was for her to toil, a slave with heavy irons on her feet, in her Master's fields and pleasure-grounds, and these gowned men with shaven heads, wearing ropes of beads and crucifixes as emblems of their authority — these were the taskmasters set over her, and to these, she, Elfrida, one time queen in England, would bend in submission and humbly confess her sins, and uncomplainingly take whatever austerities or other punishments they decreed.

Here, then, at Amesbury itself, she began her work of expiation, and found that she, too, like the unhappy man in the parable, could experience some relief and satisfaction in her solitary embittered existence in the work itself.

Having been told that at this village where she was living a monastery had existed and had been destroyed in the dreadful wars of two or three cen-turies ago, she conceived the idea of founding a new one, a nunnery, and endowing it richly, and ac-cordingly the Abbey of Amesbury was built and generously endowed by her.

This religious house became famous in after days, and was resorted to by the noblest ladies in the land who desired to take the veil, including princesses and widow queens; and it continued to flourish for centuries down to the Dissolution.

This work completed, she returned, after nineteen years, to her old home at Wherwell. Since she had lost sight of her maid Editha, she had been possessed with a desire to revisit that spot, where she had been happy as a young bride and had repined in solitude and had had her glorious triumph and stained her soul with crime. She craved for it again, especially to look once more at the crystal current of the Test in which she had been accustomed to dip her hands. The grave, saintly face of Editha had reminded her of that stream; and Editha she might not see. She could not seek for her, nor speak to her, nor cry to her to come back to her, since she had said that they would meet no more on earth.

Having become possessed of the castle which she had once regarded as her prison and cage, she ordered its demolition and used the materials in building the abbey she founded at that spot, and it was taken for granted by the Church that this was done in expiation of the part she had taken in Athelwold's murder. And at this spot where the stream had become associated in her mind with the thought of Editha, and was a sacred stream, she resolved to end her days. But the time of her retirement was not yet, there was much still waiting for her to do in her Master's fields and pleasure-grounds. For no sooner had the tidings of her work in founding these monasteries and the lavish use she was making of her great wealth been spread abroad, than from many religious houses all over the land the cry was sent to her—the Macedonian cry to St. Paul to come over and help us.

From the houses founded by Edgar the cry was particularly loud and insistent. There were forty-seven of them, and had not Edgar died so soon there would have been fifty, that being the number he had set his heart on in his fervid zeal for religion. All, alas! were insufficiently endowed; and it was for Elfrida, as they were careful to point out, to increase their income from her great wealth, seeing that this would enable them to associate her name with that of Edgar and keep it in memory, and this would be good for her soul.

To all such calls she listened, and she performed many and long journeys to the religious houses all over the country to look closely into their conditions and needs, and to all she gave freely or in moderation, but not always without a gesture of scorn. For in her heart of hearts she was still Elfrida and unchanged, albeit outwardly she had attained to humility; only once during these years of travel and toil when she was getting rid of her wealth did she allow her secret bitterness and hostility to her ecclesiastical guides and advisers to break out.

She was at Worcester, engaged in a conference with the bishop and several of his clergy; they were sitting at an oak table with some papers and plans before them, when the news was brought into the room that Archbishop Dunstan was dead.

They all, except Elfrida, started to their feet with looks and exclamations of dismay as if some frightful calamity had come to pass. Then dropping upon their knees with bowed heads and lifted hands they prayed for the repose of his soul. They prayed silently, but the silence was broken by a laugh from the queen. Starting to his feet the bishop turned on her a severe countenance, and asked why she laughed at that solemn moment.

She replied that she had laughed unthinkingly, as the linnet sings, from pure joy of heart at the glad tidings that their holy archbishop had been translated to paradise. For if he had done so much for England when burdened with the flesh, how much more would he be able to do now from the seat or throne to which he would be exalted in heaven in virtue of the position his blessed mother now occupied in that place.

The bishop, angered at her mocking words, turned his back on her, and the others, following his example, averted their faces, but not one word did they utter.

They remembered that Dunstan in former years, when striving to make himself all-powerful in the kingdom, had made free use of a supernatural machinery; that when he wanted a thing done and it could not be done in any other way, he received a command from heaven, brought to him by some saint or angel, to have it done, and the command had then to be obeyed. They also remembered that when Dunstan, as he informed them, had been

snatched up into the seventh heaven, he did not
on his return to earth say modestly, like St. Paul,
that it was not lawful for him to speak of the things
which he had heard and seen, but he proclaimed
them to an astonished world in his loudest trumpet
voice.   Also, that when, by these means, he had
established his power and influence and knew that
he could trust his own subtle brains to maintain his
position, he had dropped the miracles and visions.
And it had come to pass that when the archbishop
had seen fit to leave the supernatural element out of
his policy, the heads of the Church in England were
only too pleased to have it so.   The world had gaped
with astonishment at these revelations long enough,
and its credulity had come near to the breaking
point, on which account the raking up of these
perilous matters by the queen was fiercely resented.

But the queen was not yet satisfied that enough
had been said by her.   Now she was in full revolt
she must give out once for all the hatred of her old
enemy, which his death had not appeased.

"What mean you, Fathers," she cried, "by turning
your backs on me and keeping silent?   Is it an
insult to me you intend or to the memory of that
great and holy man who has just quitted the earth?
Will you dare to say that the reports he brought
to us of the marvellous doings he witnessed in
heaven, when he was taken there, were false and
the lies and inventions of Satan, whose servant
he was?"

More than that she was not allowed to say, for

now the bishop in a mighty rage swung round, and dealing a blow on the table with such fury that his arm was disabled by it, he shouted at her: "Not another word! Hold your mocking tongue, fiendish woman!" Then, plucking up his gown with his left hand for fear of being tripped up by it, he rushed out of the room.

The others, still keeping their faces averted from her, followed at a more dignified pace; and seeing them depart she cried after them: "Go, Fathers, and tell your bishop that if he had not run away so soon he would have been rewarded for his insolence by a slap in the face."

This outburst on her part caused no lasting break in her relations with the Church. It was to her merely an incident in her long day's toil in her Master's fields—a quarrel she had had with an overseer; while he, on his side, even before he recovered the use of his injured arm, thought it best for their souls, as well as for the interests of the Church, to say no more about it. Her great works of expiation were accordingly continued. But the time at length arrived for her to take her long-desired rest before facing the unknown dreaded future. She was not old in years, but remorse and a deep settled melancholy and her frequent fierce wrestlings with her own rebellious nature as with an untamed dangerous animal chained to her had made her old. Furthermore, she had by now well-nigh expended all her possessions and wealth, even to the gems she had once prized and then thrust away out of sight for

many years, and which her maid Editha had rejected
with scorn, saying they were no more to her than
pebbles from the brook.

Once more at Wherwell, she entered the Abbey,
and albeit she took the veil herself she was not under
the same strict rule as her sister nuns. The Abbess
herself retired to Winchester and ruled the convent
from that city, while Elfrida had the liberty she
desired, to live and do as she liked in her own rooms
and attend prayers and meals only when inclined to
do so. There, as always, since Edward's death, her
life was a solitary one, and in the cold season she
would have her fire of logs and sit before it as in the
old days in the castle, brooding ever on her happy
and unhappy past and on the awful future, the years
and centuries of suffering and purification.

It was chiefly this thought of the solitariness of
that future state, that companionless way, centuries
long, that daunted her. Here in this earthly state,
darkened as it was, there were yet two souls she
could and constantly did hold communion with—
Editha still on earth, though not with her, and
Edward in heaven; but in that dreadful desert to
which she would be banished there would be a great
gulf set between her soul and theirs.

But perhaps there would be others she had known,
whose lives had been interwoven with hers, she
would be allowed to commune with in that same
place. Edgar of a certainty would be there, although
Glastonbury had built him a chapel and put him
in a silver tomb and had begun to call him Saint

Edgar. Would he find her and seek to have speech with her? It was anguish to her even to think of such an encounter. She would say: "Do not come to me, for rather would I be alone in this dreadful solitude for a thousand years than have you, Edgar, for company. For I have not now one thought or memory of you in my soul that is not bitter. It is true that I once loved you: even before I saw your face I loved you, and said in my heart that we two were destined to be one. And my love increased when we were united, and you gave me my heart's desire—the power I loved, and glory in the sight of the world. And although in my heart I laughed at your pretended zeal for a pure religion while you were gratifying your lower desires and chasing after fair women all over the land, I admired and gloried in your nobler qualities, your activity and vigilance in keeping the peace within your borders, and in making England master of the seas, so that the pirate kings of the North ventured not to approach our shores. But on your own gross appetites you would put no restraint, but gave yourself up to wine and gluttony and made a companion of Death; even in the flower of your age you were playing with Death, and when you had lived but half your years you rode away with Death and left me alone; you, Edgar, the mighty hunter and slayer of wolves, you rode away and left me to the wolves, alone, in a dark forest. Therefore the guilt of Edward's death is yours more than mine, though my soul is stained red with his blood, seeing that you left me to fight alone, and in my madness, not knowing what I did, I stained myself with this crime.

"But what you have done to me is of little moment, seeing that mine is but one soul of the many thousands that were given into your keeping, and your crime in wasting your life for the sake of base pleasures was committed against an entire nation, and not of the living only but also the great and glorious dead of the race of Cerdic—of the men who have laboured these many centuries, shedding their blood on a hundred stricken fields, to build up this kingdom of England; and when their mighty work was completed it was given into your hands to keep and guard. And you died and abandoned it; Death, your playmate, has taken you away, and Edgar's peace is no more. Now your ships are scattered or sunk in the sea, now the invaders are again on your coasts as in the old dreadful days, burning and slaying, and want is everywhere and fear is in all hearts throughout the land. And the king, your son, who inherited your beautiful face and nought beside except your vices and whatever was least worthy of a king, he too is now taking his pleasure, even as you took yours, in a gay bejewelled dress, with some shameless woman at his side and a wine-cup in his hand. O unhappy mother that I am, that I must curse the day a son was born to me! O grief immitigable that it was my deed, my dreadful deed, that raised him to the throne—the throne that was Alfred's and Edmund's and Athelstan's!"

These were the thoughts that were her only

G

company as she sat brooding before her winter fire, day after day, and winter following winter, while the years deepened the lines of anguish on her face and whitened the hair that was once red-gold.

But in the summer time she was less unhappy, for then she could spend the long hours out of doors under the sky in the large shaded gardens of the convent with the stream for boundary on the lower side. This stream had now become more to her than in the old days when, languishing in solitude, she had made it a companion and confidant. For now it had become associated in her mind with the image of the maid Editha, and when she sat again at the old spot on the bank gazing on the swift crystal current, then dipping her hand in it and putting the wetted hand to her lips, the stream and Editha were one.

Then one day she was missed, and for a long time they sought for her all through the building and in the grounds without finding her. Then the seekers heard a loud cry, and saw one of the nuns running towards the convent door, with her hands pressed to her face as if to shut out some dreadful sight; and when they called to her she pointed back towards the stream and ran on to the house. Then all the sisters who were out in the grounds hurried down to the stream to the spot where Elfrida was accustomed to sit, and were horrified to see her lying drowned in the water.

It was a hot, dry summer and the stream was low, and in stooping to dip her hand in the water she had lost her balance and fallen in, and although the water was but three feet deep she had in her feebleness been unable to save herself. She was lying on her back on the clearly seen bed of many-coloured pebbles, her head pointing downstream, and the swift fretting current had carried away her hood and pulled out her long abundant silver-white hair, and the current played with her hair, now pulling it straight out, then spreading it wide over the surface, mixing its silvery threads with the hair-like green blades of the floating water-grass. And the dead face was like marble; but the wide-open eyes that had never wholly lost their brilliance and the beautiful lungwort-blue colour were like living eyes —living and gazing through the crystal-clear running water at the group of nuns staring down with horror-struck faces at her.

Thus ended Elfrida's darkened life; nor did it seem an unfit end; for it was as if she had fallen into the arms of the maiden who had in her thoughts become one with the stream—the saintly Editha through whose sacrifice and intercession she had been saved from death everlasting.

HAWTHORN AND IVY NEAR THE GREAT RIDGE WOOD

AN OLD THORN

I

THE little village of Ingden lies in a hollow of the South Wiltshire Downs, the most isolated of the villages in that lonely district. Its one short street is crossed at right angles in the middle part by the Salisbury road, and standing just at that point, the church on one hand, the old inn on the other, you can follow it with the eye for a distance of nearly three miles. First it goes winding up the low down under which the village stands, then vanishes over the brow to reappear again a mile and a half further away as a white band on the vast green slope of the succeeding down, which rises to a height of over six hundred feet. On the summit it vanishes once more, but those who use it know it for a laborious road crossing several high ridges before dropping down into the valley road leading to Salisbury.

When, standing in the village street, your eye travels up that white band, you can distinctly make out even at that distance a small, solitary tree standing near the summit—an old thorn with an ivy growing on it. My walks were often that way, and invariably on coming to that point I would turn twenty yards aside from the road to spend half an hour seated on the turf near or under the old tree. These half-hours were always grateful; and conscious that the tree drew me to it I questioned myself as to the reason. It was, I told myself, nothing but mental curiosity: my interest was a purely scientific one. For how comes it, I asked, that a thorn can grow to a tree and live to a great age in such a situation, on a vast, naked down, where for many centuries, perhaps for thousands of years, the herbage has been so closely fed by sheep as to have the appearance of a carpet, or newly mown lawn? The seed is carried and scattered everywhere by the birds, but no sooner does it germinate and send up a shoot than it is eaten down to the roots; for there is no scent that attracts a sheep more, no flavour it has greater taste for, than that of any forest seedling springing up amidst the minute herbaceous plants which carpet the downs. The thorn, like other organisms, has its own unconscious intelligence and cunning, by means of which it endeavours to save itself and fulfil its life. It opens its first tender leaves under the herbage, and at the same time thrusts up a vertical spine to wound the nibbling mouth; and no sooner has it got a leaf or two and a spine than it spreads its roots all round, and from each of them springs a fresh shoot, leaves and protecting spine, to increase the chances of preservation. In vain! the cunning animal finds a way to defeat all this strategy, and after the leaves have been bitten off again and again, the infant plant gives up the struggle and dies in the ground. Yet we see that from time to time one survives—one perhaps in a million; but how—whether by a quicker growth or a harder or more poisonous thorn, an unpalatable leaf, or some other secret agency—we cannot guess. First as a diminutive scrubby shrub, with numerous iron-hard stems, with few and small leaves but many thorns, it keeps its poor flowerless frustrate life for perhaps half a century or longer, without growing more than a couple of feet high; and then, as by a miracle, it will spring up until its top shoots are out of reach of the browsing sheep, and in the end it becomes a tree with spreading branches and fully developed leaves, and flowers and fruit in their season.

One day I was visited by an artist from a distance who, when shown the thorn, pronounced it a fine subject for his pencil, and while he made his picture we talked about the hawthorn generally as compared with other trees, and agreed that, except in its blossoming time when it is merely pretty, it is the most engaging and perhaps the most beautiful of our native trees. We said that it was the most *individual* of trees, that its variety was infinite, for you never find two alike, whether growing in a forest, in groups, or masses, or alone. We were almost lyrical in its praises. But the solitary thorn was always best, he said, and this one was perhaps the best of all he had seen: strange and at the same time decorative in its form, beautiful too in its appearance of great age with unimpaired vigour and something more in its expression—that elusive something which we find in some trees and don't know how to explain.

Ah, yes, thought I, it was this appeal to the æsthetic

faculty which attracted me from the first, and not, as I had imagined, the mere curiosity of the naturalist interested mainly and always in the *habits* of living things, plant or animal.

Certainly the thorn had strangeness. Its appearance as to height was deceptive; one would have guessed it eighteen feet; measuring it I was surprised to find it only ten. It has four separate boles, springing from one root, leaning a little away from each other, the thickest just a foot in circumference. The branches are few, beginning at about five feet from the ground, the foliage thin, the leaves throughout the summer stained with grey, rust-red, and purple colour. Though so small and exposed to the full fury of every wind that blows over that vast naked down, it has yet an ivy growing on it—the strangest of the many strange ivy-plants I have seen. It comes out of the ground as two ivy trunks on opposite sides of the stoutest bole, but at a height of four feet from the surface the two join and ascend the tree as one round iron-coloured and iron-hard stem, which goes curving and winding snakewise among the branches as if with the object of roping them to save them from being torn off by the winds. Finally, rising to the top, the long serpent stem opens out in a flat disc-shaped mass of close-packed branchlets and twigs densely set with small round leaves, dark dull green and tough as parchment. One could only suppose that thorn and ivy had been partners from the beginning of life, and that the union was equally advantageous to both.

The small ivy disc or platform on top of the tree was a favourite stand and look-out for the downland birds. I seldom visited the spot without disturbing some of them, now a little company of missel-thrushes, now a crowd of starlings, then perhaps a dozen rooks, crowded together, looking very big and conspicuous on their little platform.

Being curious to find out something about the age of the tree, I determined to put the question to my old friend Malachi, aged eighty-nine, who was born and had always lived in the parish and had known the downs and probably every tree growing on them for miles around from his earliest years. It was my custom to drop in of an evening and sit with him, listening to his endless reminiscences of his young days. That evening I spoke of the thorn, describing its position and appearance, thinking that perhaps he had forgotten it. How long, I asked him, had the thorn been there?

He was one of those men, usually of the labouring class, to be met with in such lonely, out-of-the-world places as the Wiltshire Downs, whose eyes never look old however many their years may be, and are more like the eyes of a bird or animal than a human being, for they gaze at you and through you when you speak without appearing to know what you say. So it was on this occasion; he looked straight at me with no sign of understanding, no change in his clear grey eyes, and answered nothing. But I would not be put off, and when, raising my voice, I repeated the question, he replied, after another interval of

silence, that the thorn "was never any different."
'Twas just the same, ivy and all, when he were a
small boy. It looked just so old; why, he remembered his old father saying the same thing—'twas
the same when he were a boy, and 'twas the same
in his father's time. Then, anxious to escape from
the subject, he began talking of something else.

It struck me that after all the most interesting
thing about the thorn was its appearance of great
age, and this aspect I had now been told had continued for at least a century, probably for a much
longer time. It produced a reverent feeling in me
such as we experience at the sight of some ancient
stone monument. But the tree was alive, and because
of its life the feeling was perhaps stronger than in
the case of a granite cross or cromlech or other
memorial of antiquity.

Sitting by the thorn one day it occurred to me
that, growing at this spot close to the road and near
the summit of that vast down, numberless persons
travelling to and from Salisbury must have turned
aside to rest on the turf in the shade after that
laborious ascent or before beginning the long descent
to the valley below. Travellers of all conditions, on
foot or horseback, in carts and carriages, merchants,
bagmen, farmers, drovers, gipsies, tramps and vag-
rants of all descriptions, and from time to time
troops of soldiers. Yet never one of them had injured
the tree in any way! I could not remember ever
finding a tree growing alone by the roadside in a
lonely place which had not the marks of many old

and new wounds inflicted on its trunk with knives, hatchets, and other implements. Here not a mark, not a scratch had been made on any one of its four trunks or on the ivy stem by any thoughtless or mischievous person, nor had any branch been cut or broken off. Why had they one and all respected this tree?

It was another subject to talk to Malachi about, and to him I went after tea and found him with three of his neighbours sitting by the fire and talking; for though it was summer the old man always had a fire in the evening.

They welcomed and made room for me, but I had no sooner broached the subject in my mind than they all fell into silence, then after a brief interval the three callers began to discuss some little village matter. I was not going to be put off in that way, and, leaving them out, went on talking to Malachi about the tree. Presently one by one the three visitors got up and, remarking that it was time to be going, they took their departure.

The old man could not escape nor avoid listening, and in the end had to say something. He said he didn't know nothing about all them tramps and gipsies and other sorts of men who had sat by the tree; all he knowed was that the old thorn had been a good thorn to him—first and last. He remembered once when he was a young man, not yet twenty, he went to do some work at a village five miles away, and being winter time he left early, about four o'clock, to walk home over the downs. He had just got

married, and had promised his wife to be home for
tea at six o'clock. But a thick fog came up over the
downs, and soon as it got dark he lost himself. 'Twas
the darkest, thickest night he had ever been out in;
and whenever he came against a bank or other ob-
struction he would get down on his hands and knees
and feel it up and down to get its shape and find out
what it was, for he knew all the marks on his native
downs; 'twas all in vain—nothing could he recognise.
In this way he wandered about for hours, and was
in despair of getting home that night, when all at
once there came a sense of relief, a feeling that it was
all right, that something was guiding him.

I remarked that I knew what that meant; he had
lost his sense of direction and had now all at once
recovered it; such a thing had often happened; I
once had such an experience myself.

No, it was not that, he returned. He had not
gone a dozen steps from the moment that sense of
confidence came to him, before he ran into a tree,
and feeling the trunk with his hands he recognised
it as the old thorn and knew where he was. In a
couple of minutes he was on the road, and in less
than an hour, just about midnight, he was safe
at home.

No more could I get out of him, at all events on
that occasion; nor did I ever succeed in extracting
any further personal experience in spite of his having
let out that the thorn had been a good thorn to him,
first and last. I had, however, heard enough to
satisfy me that I had at length discovered the real

secret of the tree's fascination. I recalled other trees
which had similarly affected me, and how, long
years ago, when a good deal of my time was spent
on horseback, whenever I found myself in a certain
district I would go miles out of my way just to look
at a solitary old tree growing in a lonely place, and
to sit for an hour to refresh myself, body and soul,
in its shade. I had indeed all along suspected the
thorn of being one of this order of mysterious trees;
and from other experiences I had met with, one
some years ago in a village in this same county of
Wilts, I had formed the opinion that in many persons
the sense of a strange intelligence and possibility
of power in such trees is not a mere transitory state
but an enduring influence which profoundly affects
their whole lives.

Determined to find out something more, I went
to other villagers, mostly women, who are more
easily disarmed and made to believe that you too
know and are of the same mind with them, being
under the same mysterious power and spell. In this
way, laying many a subtle snare, I succeeded in
eliciting a good deal of information. It was, however,
mostly of a kind which could not profitably be used
in any inquiry into the subject; it simply went to
show that the feeling existed and was strong in many
of the villagers. During this inquiry I picked up
several anecdotes about a person who lived in
Ingden close upon three generations ago, and was
able to piece them together so as to make a con-
sistent narrative of his life. This was Johnnie Budd,

a farm labourer, who came to his end in 1821, a year
or so before my old friend Malachi was born. It is
going very far back, but there were circumstances
in his life which made a deep impression on the mind
of that little community, and the story had lived
on through all these years.

II

JOHNNIE had fallen on hard times when in an exceptionally severe winter season he with others had been thrown out of employment at the farm where he worked; then with a wife and three small children to keep he had in his desperation procured food for them one dark night in an adjacent field. But alas! one of the little ones playing in the road with some of her companions, who were all very hungry, let it out that she wasn't hungry, that for three days she had had as much nice meat as she wanted to eat! Play over, the hungry little ones flew home to tell their parents the wonderful news—why didn't they have nice meat like Tilly Budd, instead of a piece of rye bread without even dripping on it, when they were so hungry? Much talk followed, and spread from cottage to cottage until it reached the constable's ears, and he, already informed of the loss of a wether taken from its fold close by, went straight to Johnnie and charged him with the offence. Johnnie lost his head, and dropping on his knees confessed his guilt and begged his old friend Lampard to have mercy on him and to overlook it for the sake of his wife and children.

It was his first offence, but when he was taken from the lock-up at the top of the village street to be conveyed to Salisbury, his friends and neighbours

H   113

who had gathered at the spot to witness his removal shook their heads and doubted that Ingden would ever see him again. The confession had made the case so simple a one that he had at once been committed to take his trial at the Salisbury Assizes, and as the time was near the constable had been ordered to convey the prisoner to the town himself. Accordingly he engaged old Joe Blaskett, called Daddy in the village, to take them in his pony cart. Daddy did not want the job, but was talked or bullied into it, and there he now sat in his cart, waiting in glum silence for his passengers; a bent old man of eighty, with a lean, grey, bitter face, in his rusty cloak, his old rabbit-skin cap drawn down over his ears, his white disorderly beard scattered over his chest. The constable Lampard was a big, powerful man, with a great round, good-natured face, but just now he had a strong sense of responsibility, and to make sure of not losing his prisoner he handcuffed him before bringing him out and helping him to take his seat on the bottom of the cart. Then he got up himself to his seat by the driver's side; the last good-bye was spoken, the weeping wife being gently led away by her friends, and the cart rattled away down the street. Turning into the Salisbury road it was soon out of sight over the near down, but half an hour later it emerged once more into sight beyond the great dip, and the villagers who had remained standing about at the same spot watched it crawling like a beetle up the long white road on the slope of the vast down beyond.

Johnnie was now lying coiled up on his rug, his face hidden between his arms, abandoned to grief, sobbing aloud. Lampard, sitting athwart the seat so as to keep an eye on him, burst out at last: "Be a man, Johnnie, and stop your crying! 'Tis making things no better by taking on like that. What do you say, Daddy?"

"I say nought," snapped the old man, and for a while they proceeded in silence except for those heartrending sobs. As they approached the old thorn tree, near the top of the long slope, Johnnie grew more and more agitated, his whole frame shaking with his sobbing. Again the constable rebuked him, telling him that 'twas a shame for a man to go on like that. Then with an effort he restrained his sobs, and lifting a red, swollen, tear-stained face he stammered out: "Master Lampard, did I ever ask 'ee a favour in my life?"

"What be after now?" said the other suspiciously. "Well, no, Johnnie, not as I remember."

"An' do 'ee think I'll ever come back home again, Master Lampard?"

"Maybe no, maybe yes; 'tis not for me to say."

"But 'ee knows 'tis a hanging matter?"

"'Tis that for sure. But you be a young man with a wife and childer, and have never done no wrong before—not that I ever heard say. Maybe the judge'll recommend you to mercy. What do you say, Daddy?"

The old man only made some inarticulate sounds in his beard, without turning his head.

"But, Master Lampard, suppose I don't swing, they'll send I over the water and I'll never see the wife and children no more."

"Maybe so; I'm thinking that's how 'twill be."

"Then will 'ee do me a kindness? 'Tis the only one I ever asked 'ee, and there'll be no chance to ask 'ee another."

" I can't say, Johnnie, not till I know what 'tis you want."

"'Tis only this, Master Lampard. When we git to th' old thorn let me out o' the cart and let me stand under it one minnit and no more."

"Be you wanting to hang yourself before the trial then?" said the constable, trying to make a joke of it.

"I couldn't do that," said Johnnie, simply, "seeing my hands be fast and you'd be standing by."

"No, no, Johnnie, 'tis nought but just foolishness. What do you say, Daddy?"

The old man turned round with a look of sudden rage in his grey face which startled Lampard; but he said nothing, he only opened and shut his mouth two or three times without a sound.

Meanwhile the pony had been going slower and slower for the last thirty or forty yards, and now when they were abreast of the tree stood still.

"What be stopping for?" cried Lampard. "Get on—get on, or we'll never get to Salisbury this day."

Then at length old Blaskett found a voice.

"Does thee know what thee's saying, Master Lampard, or be thee a stranger in this parish?"

"What d'ye mean, Daddy? I be no stranger;

I've a-known this parish and known 'ee these nine years."

"Thee asked why I stopped when 'twas the pony stopped, knowing where we'd got to. But thee's not born here or thee'd a-known what a hoss knows. An' since 'ee asks what I says, I say this, 'twill not hurt 'ee to let Johnnie Budd stand one minute by the tree."

Feeling insulted and puzzled the constable was about to assert his authority when he was arrested by Johnnie's cry, "Oh, Master Lampard, 'tis my last hope!" and by the sight of the agony of suspense on his swollen face. After a short hesitation he swung himself out over the side of the cart, and letting down the tailboard laid rough hands on Johnnie and half helped, half dragged him out.

They were quickly by the tree, where Johnnie stood silent with downcast eyes a few moments; then dropping upon his knees leant his face against the bark, his eyes closed, his lips murmuring.

"Time's up!" cried Lampard presently, and taking him by the collar pulled him to his feet; in a couple of minutes more they were in the cart and on their way.

It was grey weather, very cold, with an east wind blowing, but for the rest of that dreary thirteen-miles journey Johnnie was very quiet and submissive and shed no more tears.

III

WHAT had been his motive in wishing to stand by the tree? What did he expect when he said it was his last hope? During the way up the long, laborious slope, an incident of his early years in connection with the tree had been in his mind, and had wrought on him until it culminated in that passionate outburst and his strange request. It was when he was a boy, not quite ten years old, that, one afternoon in the summer time, he went with other children to look for wild raspberries on the summit of the great down. Johnnie, being the eldest, was the leader of the little band. On the way back from the brambly place where the fruit grew, on approaching the thorn, they spied a number of rooks sitting on it, and it came into Johnnie's mind that it would be great fun to play at crows by sitting on the branches as near the top as they could get. Running on, with cries that sent the rooks cawing away, they began swarming up the trunks, but in the midst of their frolic, when they were all struggling for the best places on the branches, they were startled by a shout, and looking up to the top of the down, saw a man on horseback coming towards them at a gallop, shaking a whip in anger as he rode. Instantly they began scrambling down, falling over each other in their haste, then, picking themselves up, set off down the slope as fast as they could run. Johnnie was foremost, while close behind him came Marty, who was nearly the same age and, though a girl, almost as swift-footed, but before going fifty yards she struck her foot against an ant-hill and was thrown violently, face down, on the turf. Johnnie turned at her cry and flew back to help her up, but the shock of the fall, and her extreme terror, had deprived her for the moment of all strength, and while he struggled to raise her, the smaller children, one by one, overtook and passed them, and in another moment the man was off his horse, standing over them.

"Do you want a good thrashing?" he said, grasping Johnnie by the collar.

"Oh, sir; please don't hit me!" answered Johnnie; then looking up he was astonished to see that his captor was not the stern old farmer, the tenant of the down, he had taken him for, but a stranger and a strange-looking man, in a dark grey cloak with a red collar. He had a pointed beard and long black hair and dark eyes that were not evil yet frightened Johnnie, when he caught them gazing down on him.

"No, I'll not thrash you," said he, "because you stayed to help the little maiden, but I'll tell you something for your good about the tree you and your little mates have been climbing, bruising the bark with your heels and breaking off leaves and twigs. Do you know, boy, that if you hurt it, it will hurt you? It stands fast here with its roots in the ground and you—you can go away from it, you think. 'Tis not so; something will come out of it and follow you wherever you go and hurt and break you at last. But if you make it a friend and care for it, it will care for you and give you happiness and deliver you from evil."

Then touching Johnnie's cheeks with his gloved hand he got on his horse and rode away, and no sooner was he gone than Marty started up, and hand in hand the two children set off at a run down the long slope.

Johnnie's playtime was nearly over then, for by-and-by he was taken as farmer's boy at one of the village farms. When he was nineteen years old, one Sunday evening, when standing in the road with other young people of the village, youths and girls, it was powerfully borne on his mind that his old playmate Marty was not only the prettiest and best girl in the place, but that she had something which set her apart and far, far above all other women. For now, after having known her intimately from his first years, he had suddenly fallen in love with her, a feeling which caused him to shiver in a kind of ecstasy, yet made him miserable, since it had purged his sight and made him see, too, how far apart they were and how hopeless his case. It was true they had been comrades from childhood, fond of each other, but she had grown and developed until she had become that most bright and lovely being, while he had remained the same slow-witted,

awkward, almost inarticulate Johnnie he had always
been.   This feeling preyed on his poor mind, and
when he joined the evening gathering in the village
street he noted bitterly how contemptuously he was
left out of the conversation by the others, how in-
capable he was of keeping pace with them in their
laughing talk and banter.   And, worst of all, how
Marty was the leading spirit, bandying words and
bestowing smiles and pleasantries all round, but
never a word or a smile for him.   He could not endure
it, and so instead of smartening himself up after
work and going for company to the village street,
he would walk down the secluded lane near the
farm to spend the hour before supper and bedtime
sitting on a gate, brooding on his misery; and if
by chance he met Marty in the village he would try
to avoid her, and was silent and uncomfortable in
her presence.

After work, one hot summer evening, Johnnie
was walking along the road near the farm in his
working clothes, clay-coloured boots, and old dusty
hat, when who should he see but Marty coming
towards him, looking very sweet and fresh in her
light-coloured print gown.   He looked to this side
and that for some friendly gap or opening in the
hedge so as to take himself out of the road, but there
was no way of escape at that spot, and he had to
pass her, and so casting down his eyes he walked on,
wishing he could sink into the earth out of her sight.
But she would not allow him to pass; she put herself
directly in his way and spoke.

"What's the matter with 'ee, Johnnie, that 'ee don't want to meet me and hardly say a word when I speak to 'ee?"

He could not find a word in reply; he stood still, his face crimson, his eyes on the ground.

"Johnnie, dear, what is it?" she asked, coming closer and putting her hand on his arm.

Then he looked up, and seeing the sweet compassion in her eyes, he could no longer keep the secret of his pain from her.

"'Tis 'ee, Marty," he said. "There'll never want I—there's others 'ee'll like better. 'Tisn't for I to say a word about that, I'm thinking, for I be—just nothing. An'—an'—I be going away from the village, Marty, and I'll never come back no more."

"Oh, Johnnie, don't 'ee say it! Would 'ee go and break my heart? Don't 'ee know I've always loved 'ee since we were little mites together?"

And thus it came about that Johnnie, most miserable of men, was all at once made happy beyond his wildest dreams. And he proved himself worthy of her; from that time there was not a more diligent and sober young labourer in the village, nor one of a more cheerful disposition, nor more careful of his personal appearance when, the day's work done, the young people had their hour of social intercourse and courting. Yet he was able to put by a portion of his weekly wages of six shillings to buy sticks, so that when spring came round again he was able to marry and take Marty to live with him in his own cottage.

One Sunday afternoon, shortly after this happy event, they went out for a walk on the high down.

"Oh, Johnnie, 'tis a long time since we were here together, not since we used to come and play and look for cowslips when we were little."

Johnnie laughed with pure joy and said they would just be children and play again, now they were alone and out of sight of the village; and when she smiled up at him he rejoiced to think that his union with this perfect girl was producing a happy effect on his poor brains, making him as bright and ready with a good reply as anyone. And in their happiness they played at being children just as in the old days they had played at being grown-ups. Casting themselves down on the green, elastic, flower-sprinkled turf, they rolled one after the other down the smooth slopes of the terrace, the old "shepherd's steps," and by-and-by Johnnie, coming upon a patch of creeping thyme, rubbed his hands in the pale purple flowers, then rubbed her face to make it fragrant.

"Oh, 'tis sweet!" she cried. "Did 'ee ever see so many little flowers on the down?—'tis as if they came out just for us." Then, indicating the tiny milkwort faintly sprinkling the turf all about them, "Oh, the little blue darlings! Did 'ee ever see such a dear blue?"

"Oh, aye, a prettier blue nor that," said Johnnie. "'Tis just here, Marty," and pressing her down he kissed her on the eyelids a dozen times.

"You silly Johnnie!"

"Be I silly, Marty? but I love the red too," and with that he kissed her on the mouth. "And, Marty, I do love the red on the breasties too—won't 'ee let me have just one kiss there?"

And she, to please him, opened her dress a little way, but blushingly, though she was his wife and nobody was there to see, but it seemed strange to her out of doors with the sun overhead. Oh, 'twas all delicious! Never was earth so heavenly sweet as on that wide green down, sprinkled with innumerable little flowers, under the wide blue sky and the all-illuminating sun that shone into their hearts!

At length, rising to her knees and looking up the green slope, she cried out: "Oh, Johnnie, there's the old thorn tree! Do 'ee remember when we played at crows on it and had such a fright? 'Twas the last time we came here together. Come, let's go to the old tree and see how it looks now."

Johnnie all at once became grave, and said No, he wouldn't go to it for anything. She was curious and made him tell her the reason. He had never forgotten that day and the fear that came into his mind on account of the words the strange man had spoken. She didn't know what the words were; she had been too frightened to listen, and so he had to tell her.

"Then, 'tis a wishing-tree for sure," Marty exclaimed. When he asked her what a wishing-tree was, she could only say that her old grandmother, now dead, had told her: 'Tis a tree that knows us

and can do us good and harm, but will do good only
to some; but they must go to it and ask for its pro-
tection, and they must offer it something as well as
pray to it.   It must be something bright—a little
jewel or coloured bead is best, and if you haven't
got such a thing, a bright-coloured ribbon, or strip
of scarlet cloth or silk thread—which you must tie
to one of the twigs.

"But we hurted the tree, Marty, and 'twill do no
good to we."

They were both grave now; then a hopeful thought
came to her aid.   They had not hurt the tree inten-
tionally; the tree knew that—it knew more than
any human being.   They might go and stand side
by side under its branches and ask it to forgive
them and grant them all their desires.   But they
must not go empty-handed, they must have some
bright thing with them when making their prayer.
Then she had a fresh inspiration.   She would take
a lock of her own bright hair, and braid it with some
of his, and tie it with a piece of scarlet thread.

Johnnie was pleased with this idea, and they
agreed to take another Sunday afternoon walk and
carry out their plan.

The projected walk was never taken, for by-and-
by Marty's mother fell ill, and Marty had to be with
her, nursing her night and day.   And months went
by, and at length, when her mother died, she was
not in a fit condition to go long walks and climb
those long, steep slopes.   After the child was born,
it was harder than ever to leave the house, and

Johnnie, too, had so much work at the farm that he
had little inclination to go out on Sundays. They
ceased to speak of the tree, and their long-projected
pilgrimage was impracticable until they could see
better days. But the wished time never came, for,
after the first child, Marty was never strong. Then
a second child came, then a third; and so five years
went by, of toil and suffering and love, and the tree,
with all their hopes and fears and intentions regarding
it, was less and less in their minds, and was all but
forgotten. Only Johnnie, when at long intervals his
master sent him to Salisbury with the cart, remembered it all only too well when, coming to the top of
the down, he saw the old thorn directly before him.
Passing it, he would turn his face away not to see it
too closely, or, perhaps, to avoid being recognised
by it. Then came the time of their extreme poverty,
when there was no work at the farm and not one of
their own people to help tide them over a season of
scarcity, for the old people were dead or in the work-
house or so poor as to want help themselves. It was
then that, in his misery at the sight of his ailing
anxious wife — the dear Marty of the beautiful
vanished days—and his three little hungry children,
that he went out into the field one dark night to get
them food.

The whole sad history was in his mind as they
slowly crawled up the hill, until it came to him that
perhaps all their sufferings and this great disaster
had been caused by the tree—by that something
from the tree which had followed him, never resting

in its mysterious enmity until it broke him. Was it too late to repair that terrible mistake? A gleam of hope shone on his darkened mind, and he made his passionate appeal to the constable. He had no offering—his hands were powerless now; but at least he could stand by it and touch it with his body and face and pray for its forgiveness, and for deliverance from the doom which threatened him. The constable had compassionately, or from some secret motive, granted his request; but alas! if in very truth the power he had come to believe in resided in the tree, he was too late in seeking it.

The trial was soon over; by pleading guilty Johnnie had made it a very simple matter for the court. The main thing was to sentence him. By an unhappy chance the judge was in one of his occasional bad moods; he had been entertained too well by one of the local magnates on the previous evening and had sat late, drinking too much wine, with the result that he had a bad liver, with a mind to match it. He was only too ready to seize the first opportunity that offered—and poor Johnnie's case was the first that morning—of exercising the awful power a barbarous law had put into his hands. When the prisoner's defender declared that this was a case which called loudly for mercy, the judge interrupted him to say that he was taking too much upon himself, that he was, in fact, instructing the judge in his duties, which was a piece of presumption on his part. The other was quick to make a humble apology and to bring his perfunctory address to a conclusion. The judge, in addressing the prisoner, said he had been unable to discover any extenuating circumstances in the case. The fact that he had a wife and family dependent on him only added to his turpitude, since it proved that no consideration could serve to deter him from a criminal act. Furthermore, in dealing with this case, he must take into account the prevalence of this particular form of crime; he would venture to say that it had been encouraged by an extreme leniency in many cases on the part of those whose sacred duty it was to administer the law of the land. A sterner and healthier spirit was called for at the present juncture. The time had come to make an example, and a more suitable case than the one now before him could not have been found for such a purpose. He would accordingly hold out no hope of a reprieve, but would counsel prisoner to make the best use of the short time remaining to him.

Johnnie standing in the dock appeared to the spectators to be in a half-dazed condition—as dull and spiritless a clodhopper as they had ever beheld. The judge and barristers, in their wigs and robes and gowns, were unlike any human beings he had ever looked on. He might have been transported to some other world, so strange did the whole scene appear to him. He only knew, or surmised, that all these important people were occupied in doing him to death, but the process, the meaning of their fine phrases, he could not follow. He looked at them, his glazed eyes travelling from face to face, to be fixed finally on the judge, in a vacant stare; but he scarcely saw them, he was all the time gazing on, and his mind occupied with, other forms and scenes invisible to the court. His village, his Marty, his dear little playmate of long ago, the sweet girl he had won, the wife and mother of his children, with her white, terrified face, clinging to him and crying in anguish: "Oh, Johnnie, what will they do to 'ee?" And all the time, with it all, he saw the vast green slope of the down, with the Salisbury road lying like a narrow white band across it, and close to it, near the summit, the solitary old tree.

During the delivery of the sentence, and when he was led from the dock and conveyed back to the prison, that image or vision was still present. He sat staring at the wall of his cell as he had stared at the judge, the fatal tree still before him. Never before had he seen it in that vivid way in which it appeared to him now, standing alone on the vast green down, under the wide sky, its four separate boles leaning a little way from each other, like the middle ribs of an open fan, holding up the wide-spread branches, the thin, open foliage, the green leaves stained with rusty brown and purple; and the ivy, rising like a slender black serpent of immense length, springing from the roots, winding upwards, and in and out, among the grey branches, binding them together, and resting its round, dark cluster of massed leaves on the topmost boughs. That green disc was the ivy-serpent's flat head and was the head of the whole tree, and there it had its eyes, which gazed for ever over the wide downs, watching all

I

living things, cattle and sheep and birds and men in their comings and goings; and although fast-rooted in the earth, following them, too, in all their ways, even as it had followed him, to break him at last.

POSTSCRIPT

TO
DEAD MAN'S PLACK
& AN OLD THORN

I

DEAD MAN'S PLACK

ONE of my literary friends, who has looked at the *Dead Man's Plack* in manuscript, has said by way of criticism that Elfrida's character is veiled. I am not to blame for that; for have I not already said, by implication at all events, in the Preamble, that my knowledge of her comes from outside. Something, or, more likely, *Somebody*, gave me her history, and it has occurred to me that this same Somebody was no such obscurity as, let us say, the Monk John of Glastonbury, who told the excavators just where to look for the buried chapel of Edgar, king and *saint*. I suspect that my informant was someone who knew more about Elfrida than any mere looker-on, monk or nun, and gossip-gatherer of her own distant day; and this suspicion or surmise was suggested by the following incident:

After haunting Dead Man's Plack, where I had my vision, I rambled in and about Wherwell on account of its association, and in one of the cottages in the village I became acquainted with an elderly widow, a woman in feeble health, but singularly attractive in her person and manner. Indeed, before making her acquaintance I had been informed by some of her relations and others in the place that she was not only the best person to seek information from, but was also the sweetest person in the village. She was a native born; her family had lived there for generations, and she was of that best South Hampshire type with an oval face, olive-brown skin, black eyes and hair, and that soft melancholy expression in the eyes common in Spanish women and not uncommon in the dark-skinned Hampshire women. She had been taught at the village school, and having attracted the attention and interest of the great lady of the place on account of her intelligence and pleasing manners, she was taken when quite young as lady's-maid, and in this employment continued for many years until her marriage to a villager.

One day, conversing with her, I said I had heard that the village was haunted by the ghost of a woman: was that true?

Yes, it was true, she returned.

Did she *know* that it was true? Had she actually seen the ghost?

Yes, she had seen it once. One day, when she was lady's-maid, she was in her bedroom, dressing or doing something, with another maid. The door was closed, and they were in a merry mood, talking and laughing, when suddenly they both at the same moment saw a woman with a still, white face walking through the room. She was in the middle of the room when they caught sight of her, and they both screamed and covered their faces with their hands.

So great was her terror that she almost fainted; then in a few moments when they looked the apparition had vanished. As to the habit she was wearing, neither of them could say afterwards what it was like: only the white, still face remained fixed in their memory, but the figure was a dark one, like a dark shadow moving rapidly through the room.

If Elfrida then, albeit still in purgatory, is able to revisit this scene of her early life and the site of that tragedy in the forest, it does not seem to me altogether improbable that she herself made the revelation I have written. And if this be so, it would account for the *veiled* character conveyed in the narrative. For even after ten centuries it may well be that all the coverings have not yet been removed, that although she has been dropping them one by one for ages, she has not yet come to the end of them. Until the very last covering, or veil, or mist is removed it would be impossible for her to be absolutely sincere, to reveal her inmost soul with all that is most dreadful in it. But when that time comes, from the very moment of its coming she would cease automatically to be an exiled and tormented spirit.

If, then, Elfrida is herself responsible for the narrative, it is only natural that she does not appear in it quite as black as she has been painted. For the monkish chronicler was, we know, the Father of Lies, and so indeed in a measure are all historians and biographers, since they cannot see into hearts and motives or know all the circumstances of the case. And in this case they were painting the picture of their hated enemy and no doubt were not sparing in the use of the black pigment.

To know all is to forgive all, is a good saying, and enables us to see why even the worst among us can always find it possible to forgive himself.

I WAS pleased at this opportunity of rescuing this story from a far-back number of the *English Review*, in which it first appeared, and putting it in a book. It may be a shock to the reader to be brought down from a story of a great king and queen of England in the tenth century to the obscure annals of a yokel and his wife who lived in a Wiltshire village only a century ago; or even less, since my poor yokel was hanged for sheep-stealing in 1821. But it is, I think, worth preserving, since it is the only narrative I know of dealing with that rare and curious subject, the survival of tree-worship in our own country. That, however, was not the reason of my being pleased.

It was just when I had finished writing the story of Elfrida that I happened to see in my morning paper a highly eulogistical paragraph about one of our long-dead and, I imagine, forgotten worthies. The occasion of the paragraph doesn't matter. The man eulogised was Mr. Justice Park—Sir James Allen Park, a highly successful barrister, who was judge from 1816 to his death in 1838. "As judge, though not eminent, he was sound, fair and sensible, a little irascible, but highly esteemed." He was also the author of a religious work. And that is all the particular Liar who wrote his biography in the D.N.B. can tell us about him.

It was the newspaper paragraph which reminded me that I had written about this same judge, giving my estimate of his character in my book, *A Shepherd's Life*, also that I was *thinking* about Park, the sound and fair and sensible judge, when I wrote *An Old Thorn*. Here then, with apologies to the reader for quoting from my own book, I reproduce what I wrote in 1905.

From these memories of the old villagers I turn to the newspapers of the day to make a few citations.

The law as it was did not distinguish between a case of the kind just related, of the starving, sorely-tempted Shergold, and that of the systematic thief: sheep-stealing was a capital offence and the man must be hanged, unless recommended to mercy, and we know what was meant by " mercy " in those days. That so barbarous a law existed within memory of people to be found living in most villages appears almost incredible to us; but despite the recommendations to " mercy " usual in a large majority of cases, the law of that time was not more horrible than the temper of the men who administered it. There are good and bad among all, and in all professions, but there is also a black spot in most, possibly all hearts, which may be developed to almost any extent, to change the justest, wisest, most moral men into " human devils." In reading the old reports and the expressions used by the judges in their summings-up and sentences, it is impossible not to believe that the awful power they possessed, and its constant exercise, had not only produced the inevitable hardening effect, but had made them cruel in the true sense of the word. Their pleasure in passing dreadful sentences was very thinly disguised by certain lofty conventional phrases as to the necessity of upholding the law, morality, and religion; they were, indeed, as familiar with the name of the Deity as any ranter in a conventicle, and the " enormity of the crime " was an expression as constantly used in the case of the theft of a loaf of bread, or of an old coat left hanging on a hedge, by some ill-clad, half-starved wretch, as in cases of burglary, arson, rape, and murder.

It is surprising to find how very few the real crimes were in those days, despite the misery of the people; that nearly all the " crimes " for which men were sentenced to the gallows and to transportation for life, or for long terms, were offences which would now be sufficiently punished by a few weeks', or even a few days', imprisonment. Thus in April 1825 I note that Mr. Justice Park commented on the heavy appearance of the calendar. It was not so much the number (170), of the offenders that excited his concern as it was the nature of the crimes with which they were charged. The worst crime in this instance was sheep-stealing!

Again, this same Mr. Justice Park, at the Spring Assizes at Salisbury, 1827, said that though the calendar was a heavy one, he was happy to find, on looking at the depositions of the principal cases, that they were not of a very serious character. Nevertheless he passed sentence of death on twenty-eight persons, among them being one for stealing half a crown!

Of the twenty-eight all but three were eventually reprieved, one of the fated three being a youth of nineteen, who was charged with stealing a mare and pleaded guilty in spite of a warning from the judge not to do so. This irritated the great man who had the power of life and death in his hand. In passing sentence the judge " expatiated on the prevalence of the crime of horse-stealing and the necessity of making an example. The enormity of Read's crime rendered him a proper example, and he would therefore hold out no hope of mercy towards him." As to the plea of guilty, he remarked that nowadays too many persons pleaded guilty, deluded with the hope that it would be taken into consideration and they would escape the severer penalty. He was determined to put a stop to that sort of thing; if Read had not pleaded guilty no doubt some extenuating circumstance would have come up during the trial and he would have saved his life.

There, if ever, spoke the " human devil " in a black cap!

I find another case of a sentence of transportation for life on a youth of eighteen, named Edward Baker, for stealing a pocket-handkerchief. Had he pleaded guilty it might have been worse for him.

At the Salisbury Spring Assizes in 1830 Mr. Justice Gazalee, addressing the grand jury, said that none of the crimes appeared to be marked with circumstances of great moral turpitude. The prisoners numbered one hundred and thirty; he passed sentences of death on twenty-nine, life transportations on five, fourteen years on five, seven years on eleven, and various terms of hard labour on the others.—*A Shepherd's Life*, pp. 241-4.

Johnnie Budd was done to death before my principal informants, one eighty-nine years old, the other ninety-three, were born; but in their early years they knew the widow and her three children, and had known them and their children all their lives; thus the whole story of Johnnie and Marty was familiar to them. Now, when I thought of Johnnie's case and how he was treated at the trial, as it was told me by these old people, it struck me as so like that of the poor young man Read, who was hanged because he pleaded guilty, that I at once came to the belief that it was Mr. Justice Park who had tried him. I have accordingly searched the newspapers of that day, but have failed to find Johnnie's case. I can only suppose that this particular case was probably considered too unimportant to be reported at large in the newspapers of 1821. He was just one of a number convicted and sentenced to capital punishment.

When Johnnie was hanged his poor wife travelled to Salisbury and succeeded in getting permission to take the body back to the village for burial. How she in her poverty, with her three little children to keep, managed it I don't know. Probably some of the other poor villagers who pitied and perhaps loved her helped her to do it. She did even more: she had a gravestone set above him with his name and the dates of his birth and death cut on it. And there it is now, within a dozen yards of the church door in the small old churchyard—the smallest village churchyard known to me; and Johnnie's and Marty's children's children are still living in the village.

POEMS

THE LONDON SPARROW

A HUNDRED years it seemeth since I lost thee,
O beautiful world of birds, O blessèd birds,
That come and go!—the thrush, the golden-bill
That sweetly fluteth after April rain,
In forest depths the cuckoo's mystic voice,
And in the breezy fields the yellowhammer,
And over all the mounting lark, that makes
The blue heaven palpitate with ecstasy!
Nor in this island only: far beyond
The seas encircling it swift memory flies
To other brighter lands, and leaves behind
The swallow and the dove: in hot sweet woods
The gaudy parrot screams; reedy and vast
Stretch ibis- and flamingo-haunted marshes.

I from such worlds removed to this sad world
Of London we inhabit now together,
O Sparrow, often in my loneliness,
No other friend remaining, turn to thee,
Like some imprisoned wretch, who in his cell
A cricket hears, and listening to its chirp,
Forgets the vanished sunshine and the laughter.
Not oft, O wingèd Arab of the streets,
Thou dusty little scavenger—a bird

Ambitious bard should blush to name—not oft
Canst claim such victory: for I have known
The kings and glorious nobles of the race
Whose homely mean ambassador thou art;—
Imperial-crested birds in purple clothed
And splendid scarlet, swans in bridal white,
And many a rainbow-tinted tanager.

Ah! how couldst thou thy birthright, liberty
In breezy woodlands, where were springs for thirst
And many-flavoured fruits to feed upon,
Resign for such a place?—to live long years
From nature sweet in exile voluntary,
Nourished on mouldy crumbs, ignoble bird!
Imprisoned in a lurid atmosphere
That maketh all things black and desolate,
Until, as in a coin illegible
To keenest Antiquary, lost are all
The signs that mark thy kind—the pretty gloss
That Nature gave thee clouded and confounded,
Till to the ornithologist thou art
A bird ambiguous; to others, too,
A thing offensive. Sometimes even I,
Aroused to fury by thy barrel-organ
That puts my thoughts to flight, would gladly hale
    thee
Before the magistrate. For thou hast not
The coyness of thy kind—for awful man
No veneration; noisy, impudent,
Begrimed with soot, the chimney-sweep of birds
To minds æsthetic.

                    Roughly have I used
The liberty of a friend, and yet I know
I love thee, Sparrow, and thy voice to me—
A dweller once in summer-lands—brings back
Responsive joy, as unto him that walks,
Pensive at eventide, the robin's song
'Midst wintry loneliness. Oh, my lost Muse,
If aught of thy sweet spirit is remaining
After my long neglect, in gratitude
To this my frequent, welcome visitor,
Whose little pipe from out discordant noises
Springs like a flower amidst a waste of rocks
To cheer my exile, I will strike again
The quaint and rust-corroded instrument
I played of yore, and to the Sparrow sing
My latest song, albeit now the chords
Give 'neath my touch an unfamiliar sound
To sadden me—the note of time and change.

At dawn thy voice is loud—a merry voice
When other sounds are few and faint. Before
The muffled thunders of the Underground
Begin to shake the houses, and the noise
Of eastward traffic fills the thoroughfares,
Thy voice then welcomes day. Oh what a day!—
How foul and haggard-faced! See, where she comes
In garments of the chill discoloured mists
Stealing unto the west with noiseless foot
Through dim forsaken streets. Is she not like,
As sister is to sister, unto her
Whose stained cheeks the nightly rains have wet
  K

And made them grey and seamed and desolate,
Beneath the arches of the bitter bridge?
And thou, O Sparrow, from the windy ledge
Where thou dost nestle—creaking chimney-pots
For softly-sighing branches; sooty slates
For leafy canopy; rank steam of slums
For flowery fragrance, and for starlit woods
This waste that frights, a desert desolate
Of fabrics gaunt and grim and smoke-begrimed,
By goblin misery haunted, scowling towers
Of cloud and stone, gigantic tenements
And castles of despair, by spectral gleams
Of fitful lamps illumined—from such place
Canst thou, O Sparrow, welcome day so foul?
Ay, not more blithe of heart in forests dim
The golden-throated thrush awakes, what time
The leaves a-tremble whisper to the breath,
The flowery breath, of morning azure-eyed!
Never a morning comes but I do bless thee,
Thou brave and faithful Sparrow, living link
That binds us to the immemorial past,
O blithe heart in a house so melancholy,
And keeper for a thousand gloomy years
Of many a gay tradition, heritor
Of Nature's ancient cheerfulness, for thee
'Tis ever Merry England! Never yet,
In thy companionship of centuries
With man in lurid London, didst regret
Thy valiant choice,—yea, even from the time
When all its low-roofed rooms were sweet with scents
From summer fields, where shouting children plucked

The floating lily from the reedy Fleet,
Scaring away the timid water-hen.

Awake at morn when still the wizard Sleep
Refracts from twilight mists the broken rays
Of consciousness, I hear thy lulling voice,
Like water softly warbling, or like wind
That wanders in the ancient moonlit trees.
And lo, with breezy feet I roam abroad;
Before me startled from the shadowy fern
Upsprings the antlered deer and flees away,
And moors before me open measureless
Whereon I seek for Morning washed in dews
Immaculate. To other realms I fly
To wait its coming, walking where the palms
Unmoving stand like pillars that uphold
Some hoary vast cathedral. Lift my heart
To thee, O holy daughter of the sun—
Sweet harbinger—the Dawn! The stars grow pale,
And I am fainting by the way, oppressed
With incense from a thousand forest flowers
All prescient of thy coming! Lo, how vast,
From mist and cloud the awful mountains rise,
Wherever up with incorporeal feet
I climb to meet the dead Peruvian's god!
O swift approaching glory, blind me not
With shafts ineffable! But re-awake
In me the sacred passion of the past,
Long quenched in blood by spirits uninformed
That slew thy worshippers! My senses swim,—
Sustain, or bear me back to earth! My feet

Scarce feel the rolling cloud, or touch they still
The awful summit of the world? Far, far
Beneath, the dark blue ocean moves, the waves
Lift up their lightning crests; the lonely earth
Is jubilant; the rivers laugh! the hills
In forests clothed, or soaring crowned with snow
In barren everlasting majesty,
Are all in gold and purple swathed for joy
That thou art coming!

                Vanished is my dream;
Even while I bowed and veiled my eyes before
The insufferable splendour of the sun
It vanished quite, and left me with this pale,
This phantom morning! With my dream thou fled'st,
O blithe remembrancer, and in thy flight
Callest thy prattling fellows, prompters too
Of dreams perchance, from many a cloudy roof
To flit, a noisy rain of sparrows, down
To snatch a hasty breakfast from the roads,
Undaunted by the thund'rous noise and motion:
But like the petrel—fearless, fitful seeker,
The fluctuating bird with ocean's wastes
And rage familiar, tossed with tossing billows—
So, gleaner unregarded, flittest thou—
Now, as of old, and in the years to come,
Nature's one witness, till the murmuring sound
Of human feet unnumbered, like the rain
Of summer pattering on the forest leaves,
Fainter and fainter falling 'midst the ruin,
In everlasting silence dies away.

IN THE WILDERNESS

THOU white-winged gull that far I see
    So buoyant in blue heaven soar,
        Ah, would thy wings were mine!
How swiftly would I fly this shore
    To scenes for which I pine;
Where dwells unsullied loveliness,
    With calm and peace divine,
Far in the untrodden wilderness.

My soul is sickened with the stress
Of life, nor more responds to cries
    Of those who lose or win
The things they struggle for. The prize,
    The battle's dust and din,
Alike I loathe and seek the rest
    That dwells the desert in,
Aloof from man on Nature's breast.

There earth with brighter sun is blest—
In purer dew-drops burns its beam,
    That gather here, alas!
There many a heron-haunted stream
    And many a plain I'd pass,
A thousand, thousand flowers behold
    Strew all the wayside grass
With crimson, white, and blue and gold.

There winds would sing to me, the old,
Old sea give forth a solemn sound,
    The wild birds warble mirth;
There would I stop to kiss the ground
    For very love of earth;
And swift away the years would glide,
    Like rills that have their birth
High on the soaring mountain side.

To gaze upon the prospect wide,
Oft on some jutting crag I'd lie
    When blooms its summer crown—
Pale heath and pansy's purple eye,
    The wind-flower, and the brown
And green blades of the bearded grass,
    Whose spears wave up and down,
White sparkling when the wind doth pass.

And there I'd muse and sigh, alas,
This transitory state of ours—
    Whose resting is the tomb—
To liken to such things as flowers,
    A little while that bloom
And sweets of paradise exhale
    From aisles of stormy gloom,
From wood and wold and winding vale.

For everywhere the blossoms frail
I love—to me do preachers seem,
    And have for me a speech
With many a mystic mournful theme;

And subtle things they teach—
(Not like harsh lessons writ with pen)—
   And inner sense oft reach,
That wakes not in the haunts of men.

The hoary hills I'd liken, when
The flowers in all their fissures blow—
   The rocks so seamed and grey
With all the length of years they know,
   And yet to pass away,
Not doomed like things that draw the breath
   Of life and of decay—
Unto a monument of death.

Memorial there the sleeper hath,
Whose dust before the wind like chaff
   Has long been scattered wide;
There blooms his living epitaph;
   And still while time shall glide,
Those letters blooming, fading, speak,
   Thus flourished he, thus died;
Thus bloomed, thus paled in death his cheek.

Sad are such thoughts, yet who would seek
To blot them from his spirit's page
   Who on his nothingness
Thinks not—how brief his pilgrimage?
   Oh, rather let him bless
The thoughts that teach the unwilling sight
   To look with less and less
Of terror on the coming night.

GWENDOLINE

SHOULD'ST thou come to me again
From the sunshine and the rain,
With thy laughter sweet and free—
Oh, how should I welcome thee?

Like a streamlet dark and cold,
Kindled into fiery gold,
By a sunbeam swift that cleaves
Downward through the curtained leaves—

So this darkened life of mine
Lit with sudden joy would shine;
And to greet thee I should start
With a great cry in my heart;

Back to drop again; the cry
On my trembling lips would die;
Thou would'st pass to be again
In the sunshine and the rain.

TECLA AND THE LITTLE MEN

A LEGEND OF LA PLATA

IT happened ninety years ago,
Hard by the spot where I was born,
The tragedy of little Tecla:
Scarce half a dozen hoary men
Now the maiden's name remember.
The world has changed, these ancients say,
From what it was;—the plume-like grass
That waved so high, the ostrich blue,
The wild horse and the antlered deer
Are now no more.

                    Here where the plain
Looks on the level marsh and out
Upon the waters of the Plata
An old estancia house once stood:
And I have played upon its site
In boyhood long ago, and traced
'Mong flowering weeds its old foundations.
'Twas here lived Lara and his wife
With their grown-up sons and daughters;
Happy and rich in pasture lands
And in their numerous herds and flocks.
Before the house a level plain
Bestrewn with shells spread shining white;
And often when the moon was up

Here came a troop of Little Men,
No taller than a boy of twelve,
Robust of limb and long of hair,
And wearing cloaks and broad sombreros.
From windows and from open doors
Distinctly could all see and hear them,
Sitting upon the ground in groups,
In shrill excited voices talking;
Or running to and fro; or ranged
Like cricketers about a field,
Playing their games the whole night long.
But if one ventured from the house
To walk upon their chosen field,
Straightway would they quit their game
To chase him back with hooting shrill,
Hurling showers of stones and pebbles
That rattled on the doors and roof
Like hail, and frightened those within.
Of all in Lara's house but one,
Light-hearted Tecla, feared them not.
The youngest of the daughters she,
A little maiden of fifteen,
Winsome in her wayward moods;
Her blithesomeness and beauty made
Perpetual sunshine in the house.
O merrily would Tecla laugh
When pebbles rattled on the door
To see her bearded brothers start,
And mother and sisters wax so pale,
And oft in pure capriciousness
Alone she'd venture forth to sit

A stone's throw from the gate, just on
The margin of that moonlit field;
There in the twilight would she linger
And bravely watch them by the hour,
Standing or running to and fro,
Hailing each other at their sport.

But once, one evening, trembling, pale,
Flying like a fawn pursued
By leaping hounds, flew Tecla home;
In at the open door she rushed
And clasped her mother close, and then
Crept silently away, and in
A corner sobbed herself to rest:
She would not tell what frightened her,
But from that evening nevermore
Would Tecla venture out alone,
When sunset left the world in shadow.
A month went by; then it was seen
A change had fallen on her spirits;
She was no more the merry one—
The bird that warbled all day long:
Infrequent fell her silvery laugh;
And silent, pale, with faltering steps,
And downcast eyes, she paced the floors,
Who yesterday from room to room
Danced fairy-like her blithesome measures.

"O say what ails you, daughter mine?
Imposthumes hidden, spasms, rheums,
Catarrhs and wasting calentures,

Have yielded to the juices I
Express from herbs medicinal;
Yet this most subtle malady
Still mocks your mother's love and skill."
" I have no sickness, mother, 'tis
But weakness; for I cannot eat,
Since on one day, long weeks ago,
Each morsel all at once appeared,
Even as I raised it, red with dust,
And thus till now it is with me;
And water limpid from the well,
And milk, grow turbid with red dust
When lifted to my thirsting lips,
Until I loathe all aliment."
" 'Tis but a sickly fancy, child,
Born of a weak distempered stomach
That can no longer bear strong food.
But you shall have things delicate
And easy to digest; the stream
Shall give its little silvery fish
To tempt; the marsh its painted eggs
Of snipe and dotterel; sweet curds
Made fragrant with the purple juice
Of thistle bloom I'll make for you
Each day, until the yellow root
Of the wild red vinegar-flower,
With powders made from gizzards dried
Of iron-eating ostriches,
Bring back a healthy appetite,
And make your nostrils love again
The steam of roasted armadillo."

Vain was her skill: no virtue dwelt
The wasting maiden to restore
In powders or in root. And soon
The failing footsteps ceased their rounds,
And through the long, long summer days
Her white cheek rested on her pillow.
And often when the moonlight shone
Upon her bed, she, lying still,
Would listen to the plover's cry,
And tinkling of the bell-mare's bell,
Come faintly from the dreamy distance;
Then in her wistful eyes would shine
A light that made her mother weep.

Within the wide old kitchen once
The Laras from their evening meal
Were startled by a piercing cry
From Tecla's room; and rushing in
They found her sobbing on the floor,
Trembling, as white as any ghost.
They lifted her—O easy 'twas
To lift her now, for she was light
As pining egret in their arms—
And laid her on her bed. And when
Her terror left her, and the balm
They gave had soothed her throbbing heart,
Clasped in her mother's arms she told
The story of her malady.

" Do you remember, mother mine,
How once with terror palpitating
Into the house I ran? That eve

Long had I sat beyond the gate
Listening to the shrill-voiced talking
And laughter of the Little People,
And half I wished—oh, was it wrong?—
Yet feared to join them in their games.
When suddenly on my neck I felt
A clasping arm, and in my ear
A voice that whispered: 'Tecla sweet,
A valiant little maid art thou!'
O mother, 'twas a Little Man,
And through the grass and herbage tall,
Soft stealing like a cat, he came,
And leaped upon the stone, and sat
By me! I rose and ran away;
Then fast he followed, crying out:
'Run; tell your mother you have found
A lover who will come full soon
For thee; run, run, thy sisters tell
Thou hast a lover rich in gold
And gems to make them pine with envy!'
And he has caused this weakness, mother;
And often when I lie awake
He comes to peer in at the window,
And smiles and whispers pretty things.
This night he came, and at my side,
Wearing a cloak all beautiful
With scarlet bright embroidery,
He sat and boldly played the lover."

"And what said he? The wicked imp!"
"He asked me if that yellow root

That's bitter to the taste, and all
My wise old mother's medicines,
Had made me hungry. Then he held
A golden berry to my mouth—
The fruitlet of the Camambú:
O beautiful it looked, and had
No red or grimy dust upon it!
And when I ate and found it sweet,
And asked with hungry tears for more,
He whispered pleasant promises
Of honied fruits: and then he spoke—
O mother mine, what did he mean!—
Of wanderings over all the earth,
Lit by the moon, above the dim
Vast forests; over tumbling waves,
And hills that soar beyond the clouds.
Then eagerly I started up
For joy to fly away with him
Bird-like above the world, to seek
Green realms; and in his arms he clasped
And raised me from my bed. But soon
As from a dream I screaming woke,
And strove so strongly to be free
He dropped me on the floor and fled."
"O daughter dear, how narrowly
Hast 'scaped! But not to you again
Shall come such moments perilous;
For know, O Tecla, and rejoice
That from this moment dates your cure,
Since like a wise physician I
Up to its hidden source have traced

The evil that afflicted you.
In former days the Little Men
Oft played their wicked pranks, but years
Have passed since any proof they gave
Of their maleficence, since sharp
And bitter lessons given them
By Holy Church had taught these imps
To know their place; and now I too
Shall draw against them sacred weapons."

Next morning to the Monastery
Hard by, where dwelt a brotherhood
Of Friars Dominican, was sent
A messenger, the holy men
To summon to the house of Lara—
To arm with ghostly arms and free
Fair Tecla from these persecutions.

At noon, wrapped in a dusty cloud,
Six mounted Friars came riding in,
Their steeds at furious gallop. They,
Rough men, spent no ignoble lives
In barren offices; but broke
The steeds they rode, and pastured herds
Of half-wild cattle, wide around
The ostrich and the puma hunted.
Thus boldly came they—Tecla's knights,
Armed with a flask of holy water,
Nor wanting at their leathern girdles
Long knives and pistols with brass barrels.

Forthwith the blest campaign began;
And through the house and round the house
They walked; on windows, walls and doors
Sprinkling the potent drops that keep
All evil things from entering;
And curses in a learned tongue
They hurled against the Little Men.

O gladly beat the heart within
The breast of every Lara there
For Tecla timely saved! She too
The sweet infection caught, and blest
With hope and health reviving laughed
The silvery laugh too long unheard.

And there was nothing more to do
Now but to finish day so good
With feasts and merriment. Then lambs
And sucking pigs were straightway slain
To heap the board hospitable;
While screaming over fields and ditches
Turkeys and ducks were chased to make
A rich repast. Then freely round
Travelled the mighty jugs of wine,
Till supper done the Friar Blas
Snatched the guitar: "Away," he cried,
"With chairs and tables! Let us show
The daughters of the house of Lara
That our most holy Monastery
Can give them partners for the dance!"

L

Loudly the contra-dance he played,
And sang, while standing in two rows
The ready dancers ranged themselves;
Till on her pillow Tecla smiled
To hear the strings twang merrily:
"O hasten, mother mine," she cried,
"To join the dance, and open wide
The doors so that the sounds may reach me."

And while they danced the Friar Blas
Improvised merry boastful words,
And couplets full of laughing jibes:

"Dost know how to sing, Little Man?
Come sing with a Dominican.

"O when I remember our fight
I must laugh for my victory to-night.

"There conquered you bleed and repine;
Here sing I and drink the red wine.

"I'll preach you a sermon in song—
My sermons are merry not long.

"No more to sweet Tecla aspire,
For know that your rival's a Friar.

"Not wise was your wooing, but cruel,
For who can have fire without fuel?

"Did'st lose her by making her thin?
By fattening perchance I shall win.

"For when the pale maiden gets well
I'll carry her off to my cell;

"For the labourer he looks for his hire,
And hot is the heart of the Friar."

A burst of laughter and applause
Followed the strain. Out rung a peal
Of eldritch laughter echoing theirs!
Sitting and standing, dancers clasped
In joyous attitudes, transfixed,
All silent, motionless, amazed,
They listened as it louder grew—
That laughter demoniacal—
Till jugs and glasses jingled loud
Upon the table, as when hoarse
Deep thunder rumbles near, and doors
And windows shudder in their frames,
And all the solid house is shaken
To its foundations. Slowly it died;
But even as it died they heard
A wailing cry:—far off it seemed,
Still ever growing more remote,
Until they thought 'twas but the sound
The stringed guitar, dropped on the floor,
Gave forth, upon their straining ears
Slow dying in long reverberations.

Up sprang the mother suddenly,
Giving a mighty cry, and flew
To Tecla's chamber. After her
The others trooped, and found her there
Weeping beside the empty cot,
Wringing her hands and wailing loud,
Calling on Tecla gone for ever.
In at the open window blew
The fresh night wind; and forth they peered
With straining eyes and faces white,
Their hearts with strange surmisings filled.
Only the moon they saw, ghost-like
In heaven walking: 'neath its light
Immeasurable spread the marsh,
And far off shone the sea-like river;
Only the swelling waves they heard,
Low murmuring to their listening ears
Through the deep silence of the night.

THE OLD MAN OF KENSINGTON GARDENS

A BALLAD

I

T HE earth is strown with withered leaves;
   The pale October sun
   Illumines with his waning beams
The trees of Kensington.

The sere leaves rustle 'neath my tread,—
   Few on the trees remain;
For summer hark, a sweet lament—
   The fitful robin's strain.

Too long, too long for me has been
   This dream of fourscore years;
Since now of all who walked with me
   But one in flesh appears:

And he an old mysterious man,
   Whose heart beats blithely still
When on grey cheek and hoary hair
   The wintry wind blows chill.

When float above grey clouds on clouds;
   When leaves are sere and dead;
When others walk with spirits bowed,
   With sad reluctant tread,

He has no care; his unaged heart
   Some pleasant fancy cheers;
He talks like one that's young; he laughs
   As in the vanished years.

II

Since I played here in childish glee
   O'er three score years and ten
Have passed—since first I knew him here,
   Ancient and hoary then.

An old man with a beard so white;
   While blue-eyed and so fair
Walked with him, ever at his side,
   A child of golden hair.

Oft in the shade those two I saw;
   Until, one summer day,
The old man spied me in his walk
   And called me from my play.

"Come here," cried he, "my pretty boy,
　A playmate waits you here;
And much it will my heart rejoice
　To watch your merry cheer.

"To join in merry hide-and-seek
　Too stiff and old I am,
But still my heart can skip and leap
　And frolic like a lamb."

"Is she your little daughter, sir?"
　Said I.　The old man smiled,
And said, "Can one so ancient be
　The father of a child?"

"She is your grandchild then," I urged.
　"That cannot be," he said,
And looked upon his little girl,
　And smiled and shook his head.

"Your great-granddaughter then," said I,
　"This child must surely be?"
"Too young, too young for that," he cried,
　Nor more would answer me.

A merry game at hide-and-seek
　Together then we played;
And in and out among the trees
　I chased the little maid.

And much it did that ancient man
    Rejoice our sport to see;
And like a child he clapped his hands,
    And shook his sides with glee.

And afterwards for full three years,
    On many a summer day,
I met and played with her, till we
    Had grown too old to play.

III

A youth with down upon his cheek
    I bade those two farewell,
And went abroad for seven years
    Beside the Rhine to dwell.

But when that studious time was gone,
    I sought my native shore,
And in the stately Gardens walked
    Of Kensington once more.

And there that ancient man I met,
    Still cheerful as of old,
And by the hand a child he held
    With hair that was like gold.

"Who is this pretty babe?" said I,
  "With pretty eyes so blue?"
"She is the child of that fair child
  That once played here with you.

"A babe in sooth, and not for me
  'Tis now to run about,
And in and out among the trees
  To run from her with shout.

"But by-and-by, when she has grown
  More firm and free of limb,
Some little boy my maid shall know,
  And she shall play with him.

"And I shall laugh to watch their sport;
  For though so old I am,
My heart goes skipping to and fro
  And leaping like a lamb."

I heard, yet scarcely did attend;
  My thoughts were far away—
What cared I how an old man spent
  The remnant of his day?

The fire of youth was in my heart,
  Ambition fired my mind:
I crossed the seas and England left
  A thousand leagues behind.

In courts of kings, in many a camp
   On India's sultry soil,
Full twenty stirring years I spent
   In peace and war's red toil.

Then struck at last in battle down,
   For many a night and day—
Within my breast a bleeding wound—
   A groaning wretch I lay.

And night and day I pined to gaze
   On England's shores again,
Until that journey long was made
   With peril and great pain.

IV

Upon my soil beloved at last,
   When shone the summer sun,
Once more I in the Gardens walked
   Of stately Kensington.

But changed was I, with cheeks so pale
   And hollow with disease!
How slowly I moved towards the shade
   With weak and trembling knees!

While sadly musing there I sat,
  Before my sight appeared
An ancient venerable man,
  With flowing snow-white beard.

'Twas he, that old man I had known
  In boyhood and in youth,
His babe now grown to womanhood—
  The very same in sooth!

Once more we talked beneath the trees,
  As in that long ago;
And gay and garrulous was he;
  I silent, full of woe.

His laugh was frequent, idle words
  Ran ceaseless from his tongue;
Of flowers he babbled, breeze and bird,
  And things that please the young.

I sighed in heaviness of heart,
  And sad was my reply
Of toils and wounds received in wars;
  Of coming home to die.

But still he talked and did not seem
  My words to understand;
And many times to welcome me
  He seized and shook my hand.

"O long-lost wanderer, welcome home!"
   He cried. "'Tis sweet to know
Not all are lost for evermore
   That vanished long ago.

"For sometimes, after many years,
   One comes again, a while
To linger here and gladden me
   With a remembered smile.

"But not for long: a restless fire
   Within him ever burns;
His wistful eye at eventide
   Oft to the sunset turns.

"And by-and-by, like passage birds
   That in the night depart,
He goes, nor ever more returns
   To cheer the old man's heart."

V

Each day all through the pleasant June
   I in the Gardens found
That ancient man: his voice subdued
   Grew like a soothing sound

Of babbling waters, or of leaves
  Soft rustling to the wind—
It came on me, my pain appeased,
  To hope restored my mind.

"Though light of foot no more," he cried,
  "But old and stiff I am,
My fancy swallow-like still flies,
  My heart skips like a lamb.

"'Tis sweet to listen from the green
  Old elms, at drowsy noon,
The whisper of the wind-moved leaves,
  The cushat's pleasant croon.

"And when the winter drives me home,
  The fire shall cheerly burn;
And I shall wait beside the glow
  For flowery May's return.

"When evenings lengthen, at my side
  My pretty maid shall sit,
And merrily we'll pass the time
  With tales for winter fit.

"But she, too, shortly from me goes
  To seek another's side;
For now a youth has won her love
  And she shall be his bride.

"And I must pass the time alone;
    But time ere long shall send
A troop of little ones, and soon
    My lonely days shall end.

"I'll choose the prettiest of the lot—
    A little maid—and she,
With eyes like blue forget-me-nots,
    Shall my companion be.

"And when my pretty blue-eyed maid
    Grows firm and free of limb,
A boy of gentle face I'll find
    And she shall play with him."

Thus while he gaily talked and smiled
    New dreams and wishes came;
The maiden dropped her gentle eyes
    And blushed with virgin shame.

"O ever sweetest," I exclaimed,
    "Of all earth's joys is this!
My heart beats at the sacred name
    Of dear domestic bliss!

"No longer will I waste my prime;
    I too shall have a part
In joy at last, and satisfy
    The hunger of my heart.

"Once more I'll cross the ocean wide,
    For here the fight of life
Is passing hard to fight, and I
    Have weary grown of strife.

"But half around the globe, and in
    Another hemisphere,
A better fortune I shall build—
    My peaceful home I'll rear.

"And one shall share that home with me;
    And as in May from earth
Spring fragrant flowerets, children dear
    Shall blossom on my hearth.

"They, too, shall play at hide-and-seek
    Amid the forest trees,
And roam in flowery gardens sweet
    More wild and vast than these.

"And in the autumn of my life
    They oft at day's decline
Shall gather round their hoary sire
    Beneath the spreading vine,

"To listen while he tells the tale
    Of how he long did roam,
In stormy years, in countries strange,
    Before he found a home."

I finished and the old man rose;
   "God speed!" he said, and smiled;
"Come home, my bonny child—no, no,
   You are no more a child!

"For you have grown to womanhood,
   And I perchance did dream
Of one—a little one—that soon
   Like what you were shall seem."

Among the trees they passed from sight;
   I turned to go; before
The sun had set and risen thrice
   I left my native shore.

VI

Now came a time of happiness
   To me in distant lands;
Peace smiled on me and Fortune blessed
   The labour of my hands.

Far in a flowery desert lone,
   In forest green attired—
A virgin paradise—arose
   The home so long desired.

And lord of all the land was I—
    Woods, hills and valleys fair;
And all the flocks and herds were mine
    That grazed in thousands there.

Often by breezy mountains blue,
    And forests without bound,
The flying quarry I pursued
    With horse and horn and hound.

And one with me that home did share,
    My brave and beauteous bride;
And children sweet were born like flowers
    To flourish at our side.

But woe is me! the fatal shade
    That rides the wandering blast,
And follows us in all our ways,
    Found our retreat at last.

I could not dwell upon the grave
    Of all my dear ones lost;
Once more a pilgrim in old age,
    Weary and tempest-tossed,

Sought I through many lands, o'er seas,
    The respite hard to find,
Till time and change in part appeased
    The anguish of my mind.

M

My wanderings ended where the chase,
　Life-long, of bliss began:
Here, said I, let me spend the days
　Left to so old a man.

VII

Once more I in the Gardens walked,
　Fanned by the summer breeze,
And heard the thrush that all day long
　Makes music in the trees.

As there I mused a man I met,
　Wrinkled and old, of slow
And feeble tread, and body bent,
　And beard as white as snow;

And with him, lending him support,
　A maiden sweet and grave.
He paused and looked at me, then forth
　A joyful cry he gave.

"Welcome, O long-lost friend!" cried he.
　"So many years passed o'er
Since forth you went from us, I dreamed
　You would return no more.

"It is the way with them; a while
 They take their solace here—
Maiden and youth and merry child—
 Then go I know not where.

"For seldom do these waiting eyes
 See the old face once more:
Far are they scattered—far and wide
 On many a distant shore.

"Shadows and lights and seasons change;
 The birds that to and fro
For ever wander, sing again
 The songs of long ago:

"And all things wander to and fro—
 Sun and bird and breeze—
Only the faces I have known,
 In vain I watch for these.

"My fancy follows them and sees
 Many a loving pair
In flowery groves more green than these,
 Where breathes a balmier air.

"Far off in ocean's thousand isles
 The merry children stray,
And laugh as in the vanished time
 Before they went away.

"But should they—children, man and maid—
　　Once more this side the sea
Gather from all their scattered ways,
　　More numerous would they be

"Than are the sere autumnal leaves,
　　When days grow brief and pale,
And loud roars in the Garden trees
　　The rough September gale;

"When all along the Serpentine
　　The swallows wildly fly,
Then soar aloft and scatter wide
　　Athwart the lowering sky;

"While ever and anon the clouds
　　Fling gusts of sudden rain;
And the wind roars; anon dies down,
　　Then wakes and roars again:

"And often as it roars and sways
　　The groves with giant might,
Fly wild and wide the yellow leaves
　　In cloud-like flight on flight.

"Yellow and russet leaves and brown,
　　Myriads on myriads still,
In dance tempestuous whirl about
　　And all the spaces fill.

"So filled with children, maids and men
   Would all the Gardens be,
Should they return from all far lands
   And islands of the sea.

"But they return not: fragrant trees
   Are theirs and cloudless skies:
The days wear on, they do not heed
   The ancient memories.

"And still as days and years glide on
   Old forms to new give place;
Then these depart, and other forms
   Succeed to go apace.

"O restless hearts, why will they not
   Rest here in peace with me!
What voices call them o'er the main—
   In dreams what is't they see!"

Thus as we walked the old man's speech
   Ran like a babbling stream;
And now I thought it was all real,
   Now thought it but a dream.

"What can the mystery be?" I cried:
   "I hear you speak and seem
To be awake, yet all the time
   I think it is a dream.

"I knew this spot, these elms and oaks,
   Unseen for many a year,
Yon open glade and this dim grove—
   I played in childhood here.

"But oaks and elms outlive frail man
   And flourish ages through;
The vernal green, the leaves they shed,
   They year by year renew.

"But nevermore for us the flame
   Of youth revives the heart:
For manhood comes, then hoary age,
   And soon the old depart.

"Yet you still linger, long ago
   Who should have passed from sight;
For here a child I knew you old,
   And time has made me white.

"Since last I saw you in this place,
   Oh, many a changeful year
Has fled, yet with the selfsame maid
   I find you walking here!"

The old man laughed aloud at that.
   "It is not so!" cried he;
"The dear companions of my walks
   Bide not so long with me.

"She passed from me—this gentle maid
  Will make as fair a bride—
I know not where, but far away
  Our paths have sundered wide.

"And this one has her mother's face—
  The daughter this, my friend—
And she will go the usual way,
  Our rambles soon will end.

"For now a youth with words of love
  Her gentle heart has won,
And she must quit the glades and groves
  Of pleasant Kensington.

"And when the groves are ghostly white,
  When 'neath the sombre cloud
Along the frozen Serpentine
  The merry skaters crowd,

"Beside the hearth I'll sit alone
  Through the long winter hours,
With no one near to share the glow,
  Until the time of flowers.

"But pretty flowers will come full soon;
  And when sweet children rise,
The fairest of them all I'll choose—
  One with her mother's eyes.

"And she shall my companion be
  On many a summer's day,
And I will watch her through the trees
  Glance by in blithesome play."

She turned aside her blushing face:
  The old man smiling sees;
Then from my side they passed away
  Among the Garden trees.

VIII

Now since I sought my land, these last
  Few years of life to spend—
The pale sad years that now perchance
  Are drawing to an end—

Six years have gone o'er me; yet oft
  As in the green retreat
Of stately Kensington I walk,
  That ancient man I meet.

Six years ago she left his side—
  The maid with hair like gold:
And with him totters now a child—
  A little five-year-old.

He talks on cheerful themes; his words
    Flow ceaseless from his tongue—
Of flowers he babbles, breeze and bird,
    And things that please the young.

He strays away: I sit for hours
    And listen to the wind,
And many a whispering dreamy sound
    That lulls my weary mind.

Of marble white and fretted gold,
    Before my fading eye,
The storied strange Memorial soars
    Sparkling against the sky.

Unceasing on my hearing falls,
    By distance made as low
As croon of dove, from all along
    The carriage-crowded Row

The sound of many hoofs and wheels;
    A ceaseless muffled roar,
As of a distant swelling sea
    Breaking along the shore.

It lulls my mind; it dies away;
    Now far it seems, now near:
The trees, the objects round me fade,
    And other scenes appear.

And still I hear that sound that is
  A river's rush, while I
Look on old towns—on purple hills,
  On castles floating by.

I talk beneath the linden trees
  To youth and maid I know;
Along the ancient pleasant street
  The people come and go.

They come and gather to a crowd;
  In serried ranks they form,
While ever nearer and more loud
  Is rolled the battle storm.

It dies; the smoke-cloud fades away,
  And pale, with bleeding breast,
O'er weary lands and ocean's waves
  I wander seeking rest.

And when to rest I sit me down
  'Tis 'neath the wild-wood tree;
There stands my steed, there lie my hounds,
  Worn with the chase like me.

Lo, where they come—O darling wife!
  O long-lost children dear!
Ah, wherefore have we wandered wide
  In grief this many a year!

I stretch my arms; alas, it fades—
    That vision sweet—in air!
Then with a sudden cry I wake
    And wildly round me stare.

The ancient man is sitting near:
    "Wake, dreamer, wake!" he cries.
I gaze on him, I strive to pierce
    The meaning of his eyes.

A mystic smile flits o'er his face;
    His touch is on my arm:
"I knew," he says, "that soon again
    This place would cease to charm.

"Again you dream of deserts vast
    Beyond the ocean wide:—
Oh, why have men such restless hearts!
    Why here will they not bide!

"But let them go, since go they will.
    My heart can merry be,
And like the robin blithely sing
    Apart from company."

And thus he ever speaks, and half
    In anger, half in play—
"Dream on," he cries, "of countries far,"
    Then leads his child away.

IX

When autumn draweth to a close,
　　Oft as the October sun
With transient glory lights the groves
　　Of stately Kensington,

Beneath the rustling trees I roam,
　　Although the east blows chill,
To taste the passing beams—to know
　　That I am living still.

And by my side the old man walks,
　　The maid with golden hair—
While I immersed in mournful thoughts
　　Heed not their presence there.

The sere leaves flutter on the trees,
　　They rustle 'neath my tread:
The sun declines, the slanting beams
　　A mystic glory shed.

The leaves that flutter to the earth,
　　And far-off fane and spire,
And tower and dome, a moment burn
　　With visionary fire.

"O season of black storms and tears,
   Of red and yellow leaf,
And glory of the sun's swift beams,
   Thy troubled period brief

"Full soon must end, and storm and shine
   With thee pass from me here.
The earth, the heavens infinite,
   The pale-faced dying year,

"With all their voices day and night,
   From earth, from ocean loud,
From birds that crying cleave the skies,
   From wind and rain and cloud,

"And from the sun's departing gleams
   Kindling the forests tall,
And thousand thousand withered leaves
   That whirl aloft and fall,

"Are calling, calling me to rise—
   Their voices fill my ear,
They tell me that the mournful time
   Of going forth is near.

"Often have I ere now gone forth,
   Both danger and disease
To brave, and hordes of frantic foes,
   And world-encircling seas;

"But greater dangers wait me now;
    And, oh, how shall I brave
That blacker sea! oh, there what clouds,
    What shipwreck and what grave

"Perchance, perchance are waiting me!
    Nor on this mournful shore
Is left one friend with farewell speech
    To waft me kindly o'er!"

He laughs to hear—that ancient man—
    A mocking laugh it seems!
"Yes, yes!" he cries, "I understand—
    Still dreaming the old dreams!

"You cannot rest; the dreams of isles
    And regions near the sun,
They will not let you here abide;
    And pale looks Kensington.

"Your friends have gone before, and lone
    And sere the Gardens seem:
Far off in summer-lands you roam—
    You meet them when you dream.

"What wonder? withered are the trees,
    And winds blow coldly here:
But there the spicy woods are green,
    And winterless the year.

"Rich fruits grow there: the birds are gay
    With plumes of splendid dyes:
From flower to flower the children chase
    The blue-winged butterflies.

"There people throng the sunny streets
    In gems and garments white:
Of marble are the palaces,
    And gold and malachite.

"There friends and old companions meet,
    Returned with precious spoil
From many a coast; together feast,
    And rest their hearts from toil.

"And oft from rest the bugle calls,
    To hunt in wood and glen
The tusky boar, or meet in war
    Dark hordes of savage men:

"To chase with fire and thund'rous noise
    The flying Amazon;
And of their treasured gold despoil
    The temples of the sun:

"To pass the azure mountain chains,
    Where vast volcanoes flame,
And riches seek in cities strange,
    And realms without a name.

"Then far to sail the halcyon seas,
    Full many a fragrant isle
To find, where in perpetual peace
    Dwell nations void of guile.

"There often as the wanderer's keel
    Does grate, from grots and bowers
Troop maidens forth, their foreheads wreathed
    With pearls and crimson flowers,

"Singing of peace—eternal peace,
    Within the isle of palms—
Singing a sacred melody
    That care and passion charms.

"O beauteous regions far away
    From this tempestuous shore,—
He dreams of you, and here his place
    Will know him soon no more!

"He dreams of you as others dreamed,
    He can no more delay—
Farewell. O friend of many years,
    God speed you on your way.

"We too, my child and I, shall dream
    When cheerfully does burn
The winter fire—dream eve by eve
    Of flowery May's return.

"And when the flowery May returns,
    And heaven sweetly smiles;
When flit and sing the passage birds
    The song of other climes—

"The climes for which you sadly sigh—
    Here shall we spend the hours,
And have for friends—my child and I—
    The sunshine and the flowers."

And thus he talks at day's decline,
    With words so wild and vain,
Then homeward leads his little child
    And leaves me to my pain.

X

The days are growing cold and brief,
    And sad the Gardens seem,
As over beds of fallen leaves
    I walk as in a dream.

My blood is thin and I am old;
    Wind, fog, and frost-bound earth
Now drive me shivering in to doze
    All day beside the hearth.

N

But when the season sweet revives
  With leaf and flower and bee,
When blushing maid at eventide
  Seeks here the trysting tree;

When pipes the thrush at eventide,
  Perchance I shall not hear;
For now I flutter in the wind,
  And I am pale and sere:

I flutter in the wind, for now
  The frosty winds prevail,
And on the tree of life each hour
  My hold is getting frail.

But they will come—you will not fail
  To meet them here—the old,
Old man, and pretty little maid
  With locks of shining gold.

PRINTED BY THE TEMPLE PRESS AT LETCHWORTH IN GREAT BRITAIN

Date Due
